UNITROL:

The Healing Magic of the Mind

UNITROL:

The Healing Magic of the Mind

Alfred J. Cantor, M.D.

Parker Publishing Company, Inc.
West Nyack, N. Y.

PRINTED IN THE UNITED STATES OF AMERICA

93896   B&P

Dedicated to the

UNIVERSAL BROTHERHOOD OF MAN

and to the

HEALING POWER OF GOD WITHIN EACH OF US

Dedicated by the Author
for the
UNITROL Teaching Institute
147–41 Sanford Avenue
Flushing 55, L.I., New York

A Special Word to My Readers . . .

It is a terrible thing to be alone. No one wants to be alone, especially when embarking on a new voyage of discovery—a discovery of self.

No matter what you undertake, it is wonderful to have a helping hand. As you seek the power that can be yours through UNITROL, there is a helping hand to guide you.

The human helping hand is mine. With every word you read throughout this book, I want you to feel your hand in mine. I want you to know that your problem is my problem. I want you to know that I am with you every step of the way. I want you to know that I, too, have suffered deeply and intensely, both physically and emotionally, and I have found my way back.

And now I want to be your guide—your helping hand.

Alfred J. Cantor, M.D.

How UNITROL Can Change Your Life

UNITROL can bring you more energy, better health, lasting peace of mind. New youth and vitality can be yours through the miracle of UNITROL.

UNITROL can change your temperament, your character, your attitudes towards life. UNITROL can eliminate your neurosis. UNITROL can improve your memory span and help you utilize your full thinking capacity, for you are now using only a tiny fraction of your mind. UNITROL can improve your sex life, your general body functions, your capacity for the enjoyment of life.

Through UNITROL you will learn how to control the voluntary muscles of your body. The capacity for instant relaxation of muscles and mind tension will be your reward.

You will also learn to control involuntary muscles in your body. When you become truly efficient in UNITROL you will be able to slow your heart rate on command. You will be able to relax spastic muscles in your intestinal tract. You will be able to lower your blood pressure.

Relaxation of your intestinal tract muscles will result in better intestinal tract function, better digestion, and better utilization of all food. This, in turn, will have a rejuvenating effect upon your entire body. Indeed, as you develop your capacity in UNITROL even further, you will slow the aging process and initiate rejuvenation.

If you are overweight, UNITROL will release you from the bondage of your excess pounds.

You will be able to control and prevent the pain of psychosomatic illness. UNITROL gives you a potent weapon for the

7

relief of symptoms, the reversal of disease, the control of many organic as well as functional tissue changes, the prolongation of life.

UNITROL may completely or partially release you from the bondage of drugs that you now use for pain or insomnia. It will restore confidence and pleasure in living, restore mental and physical equilibrium, make you younger, and prolong your life.

How UNITROL Differs
From Other Self-Help Programs

There are many books dealing with self-improvement, but in all the systems, the most significant part is overlooked. This is the **language** which we all use! We depend on language for thoughts, for ideas and, for the most part, we think in words. Yet we overlook their influence **on us.**

When you speak, when you think, you use words. And from your earliest days you build up certain responses to words. For instance, consider your reactions to the words **mother, death, cancer,** and **daisy.** Each of these words set off what is, in reality, a chain of neurological and physiological responses which only you can fully understand. One might respond to **mother** with the word **love** or **security,** to **death** or **cancer** with **fear** or **pain,** to **daisy** with **pretty.** So you see that words trigger more words in your mind—**response words** that are a kind of shorthand for the complex response you have to the initial, or **stimulus,** words (**mother, death,** etc.).

Now, if we react to words in terms of other words—if words set off certain responses in us—why can't we train ourselves to respond in certain ways that **we decide** upon?

Some people respond to the word **money** as if it were **cancer.** By this I mean that upon hearing **money,** they become anxious, fearful, and may even feel psychic pain if they think they do not have a big enough bank account. This is an extreme example, but it is by no means exceptional. This emotional reaction to the word **money** is an **improper response to a word.**

You can probably think, right now, of many words that upset you. This is a good time to jot down on a sheet of paper all such words that you think of. Later on, after you finish your UNITROL lessons, you can go back to this list and pick out the words to which you respond improperly (by **improperly,** I mean having a reaction which is not suited to what the word stands for). You will see that in many cases you were putting too much value on a word. Through UNITROL you will have learned how to control your total reaction to language and, most important, you will be aware that language is something which you can use to help yourself.

The Source of UNITROL Power

This is only one of the benefits of UNITROL, for a most important part of the UNITROL system is that you will learn to use the God-given power within you. Each human being possesses a part of God, a part of the Divine Intelligence which guides the universe.

However, most men do not realize that they have this power within them. They do not know the truth that can make them free—free from animal-like servitude to nature and their nervous systems. Men are more than animals; our possession of a highly developed language easily proves this. But men can surpass themselves, and UNITROL will show you how this can be done.

To Sum It Up . . .

UNITROL is an application of the principles of medicine that have been overlooked through the centuries. It is essential that UNITROL be used as an adjunct to your physician's diagnosis and treatment. It does not replace your trusted family physician, the consultant, specialist, or surgeon. It is an extension of the concepts of psychosomatic medicine and the insights of a universal philosophy.

UNITROL has unlimited potentialities. It can help you to:

1. Achieve a happier, more satisfying life.
2. Overcome your fears.
3. Understand your inner self and recognize your real desires.
4. Control pain and improve your health.
5. Improve your relations with others.
6. Enjoy youth and vitality.
7. Get rid of tension.
8. Make you stronger in mind and body.
9. Begin a new life being the kind of person that you always wanted to be!

As the poet Tennyson said, " 'Tis not too late to seek a newer world."

UNITROL can help you find it!

Ailments Which Can, in Many Cases, be Greatly Relieved Through the Proper Use of UNITROL

ALLERGIES
Anorexia (loss of appetite)
ANXIETY
ARTHRITIC PAIN
Asthma
Constipation
Diarrhea
Eczema
Excessive Perspiration
FATIGUE
Frigidity
Functional Sterility
GENERAL JOINT AND MUSCLE ACHES AND PAINS
Hayfever
HEADACHE
HEART DISEASE—Prevention and Control
Hiccoughs
Hives
HYPERTENSION: Some forms
Hysteria
Impotence
INDIGESTION
Inflammation of the Stomach
INSOMNIA
Menopausal Problems
Menstrual Problems
MENTAL DEPRESSION
Migraine
Mucous Colitis
NAILBITING
NERVOUS TENSION
Nervous Vomiting
Neurodermatitis
NEUROSES
OBESITY
Peptic Ulcer
Premenstrual Tension
Pruritus
Psoriasis
Psychoneurosis
RHEUMATISM
Rose Fever
Spasms
Stammering
Stuttering
Tachycardia
Tics
Ulcerative Colitis
Urinary Retention of Psychogenic Origin
Urticaria

Contents

I. UNITROL DYNAMICS

1. What UNITROL Is and What It Can Do for You   21

What UNITROL Is 22
The Miracle of Voluntary Muscle Control 22
You Can Break the Tension Chain 23
*Understanding How Your Involuntary Muscles
    Work 24*
*How UNITROL Gives You Command of All Your
    Muscles 25*
*How Psychosomatic Illness Affects Your Mind-
    Body Unit 27*
*Learn How to Throw Away Your Tranquilizers
    with UNITROL 28*
UNITROL Is More Than Muscle Control 29
How to Unleash Your Secret Inner Power 29
The Healing Force of Your God-Power 31
To Sum It Up . . . 32

2. How To Make Words Work as Your Own Magic Healers   33

Learn to Work with Your Nervous System 33
Keep Your Head and Keep Your Health 34
What Words Can Do To You 35
How Words Affect Your Health 37
Don't Trick Yourself 38
*How To Make Words Work for You with UNI-
    TROL 38*
Think Twice and Save Your Life 40
*How To Use the Indexing Technique and Escape
    Anxiety 41*

2. How To Make Words Work as Your Own Magic
Healers—Continued

> *How To Use the Dating Technique to Really See
> and Understand Yourself Now 42*
> *To Sum It Up . . . 44*

3. Using the Key Word Technique For Health Con-
trol   45

> *How to Feel Tension in Your Muscles 45*
> *How to Recognize a Relaxed Muscle 46*
> *Finding Tension in Your Forehead and Cheek
> Muscles 46*
> *How Voluntary Muscle Tension Affects Your Emo-
> tions 47*
> *How to Relax for Health 49*
> *Tension Testing and Relaxation 50*
> *UNITROL Basic Command Technique 51*
> *How to Achieve Key Word Control 52*
> *The Secret of Depth Relaxation 53*
> *How to Relax—From the Neck Down 54*
> *To Sum It Up . . . 55*

4. Unlock Your Subconscious Storehouse and
Empty Your Problem Pockets   57

> *The Special Language of Your Subconscious
> Mind 58*
> *How to Teach Your Subconscious Mind 58*
> *Never Say If 59*
> *How to Tap the Power of Your Subconscious 59*
> *How the Pendulum Technique Tells You About
> Yourself 61*
> *To Sum It Up . . . 68*

5. Controlling Your Future Health With The Pro-
jection Method   71

> *Dial "S" for Subconscious 71*
> *How to Create and Control Your Future Through
> the Projection Method 73*
> *The Secret Language of the Body 74*
> *You Ask the Questions 75*

5. Controlling Your Future Health With The Projection Method—Continued

A Simple Case Made Complex—by the Wrong Belief 76

Two Therapies that Help You Project a Fuller Life 78

How Expectation Therapy Can Work for You 78

A Brighter Life Through Enthusiasm Therapy 80

To Sum It Up . . . 81

6. How To Master Involuntary Muscle Control   83

How the Subconscious Controls the Involuntary Muscle System 83

She Was "Talked" into Heart "Disease" 85

Smooth Muscle Control—What It Is and What It Does 87

Take a Lesson from the Bear 88

How Adaptation Therapy Revitalizes You 89

To Sum It Up . . . 89

7. How Guided Association Therapy Helps You Discover The Secret Behind Your Sickness   91

How to Reach the Silent Level 91

Rid Yourself of Dangerous Emotions 92

How Guided Association Therapy Works 93

Why Guided Association Is "Different" 94

How Your Silent Level Can Help or Hurt You 95

Your Personal Recording 96

Let the Silent Level Work for You 97

Learn the Three Steps for Self-Understanding 98

How Old Are Your Problems? 100

Learn to Examine Your Life Situation 101

The Truth About Your Problems 102

The Vital Steps of Guided Association Therapy 103

The Importance of Full Feeling 104

Let Key Words Guide Your Thoughts and Solve Problems 105

How to Find the Secret Behind Your Sickness 106

How to Stop Being "Hypnotized" by the Past 108

To Sum It Up . . . 109

8. How To Make Selective Amnesia Work For You   111

Not All Memories Are Good   112
The Power of the Present   113
Learn to Count Your Blessings   114
Learn to Live with Life   116
Carry a Full Schedule Every Day   117
Learn to Use Smile Words   118
*Discard Painful Memories with the File-and-Forget
  Method   119*
Stop Living in the Past   120
To Sum It Up . . .   122

**II. USING UNITROL TO RID YOURSELF OF SICK-
NESS, WORRY, AND PAIN**

9. How To Conquer Anxiety With UNITROL   125

Learn to Live One Heartbeat at a Time   126
Chart Your Worries Away   128
Kill Worry Before It Kills You   129
How to Conquer Your Specific Anxiety   131
The Big Problem: Money   131
Health "Worries" and How to Stop Them   133
How to Ease Domestic Tensions   135
To Sum It Up . . .   136

10. How To Reduce Anguish and Pain   137

The Secret of Pain Diversion   138
The Power of Positive Affirmation   139
How to Practice Pain-Relieving Technique   140
The Magic Key to Pain Relief   141
*How to Overcome Pain with UNITROL Projection
  Technique   141*
*How to Understand the Role of Pain in Your
  Life   143*
Using the Switch Technique to Control Pain   144
How to Use UNITROL in Place of Anesthetics   144
*Anesthetized by the Subconscious: A Case His-
  tory   146*
Your Anesthetic Technique   147
Anesthesia: When and Where You Need It   148
To Sum It Up . . .   149

11. Applying UNITROL To Relieve Sickness and Suffering 151

Allergy—Its Cause and Cure 152
How to Prevent and Control Heart Disease 154
How to Relieve General Joint and Muscle Pains with UNITROL 157
"Nerves" and Other Psychological Ailments Can Be Overcome 158
How .to Combat Genito-Urinary Tract Ailments 160
You Can Control Stomach and Digestive Tract Problems 161
Not All Psychological 162

12. How To Overcome Insomnia and Add Life To Your Years 165

How to Fall Asleep Without Effort 166
The Magic Key to Help You Unlock the Door to Sleep 167
How to Add Hours to Each Day 168
How to Sleep 170
Your "Quick Sleep" System 171
To Sum It Up . . . 172

13. UNITROL: Your Drink From the Fountain of Youth 173

The Man Who Decided to Die 174
How to Find Youth Through the UNITROL T.D. 175
Launch an Enthusiasm Effort 176
See Yourself Young 177
Take a Drink of Youth 178
How UNITROL Hibernation Rejuvenates You 179
Breathe Yourself Young 181
A Final Word . . . 181

Index 185

1

UNITROL DYNAMICS

chapter 1

What UNITROL Is and What It Can Do For You

In order to understand UNITROL, you must remember that until very recently even physicians considered mind and body as separate entities. They therefore spoke of mental diseases (diseases of the mind) and somatic diseases (diseases of the body). With the development of psychosomatic medicine physicians finally realized that it is impossible to separate the mind from the body. Indeed, any such separation of mind and body is artificial.

The mind cannot exist without the body. You cannot have a body without some kind of "mind." True, mental activity is to a large extent a function of the brain and other parts of the nervous system, just as the passing of urine is a function of the kidneys, and the secretion of bile a function of the liver. However, the mind (in terms of the nervous system) is intimately dependent upon and related to the blood supply to the brain, glandular secretions circulating in the blood stream, and every other single element of the body. Mind and body are one unit, and the separation does not exist in fact, but only on a verbal level.

It is only for convenience that we use the words **mind** and **body.** These are verbal distinctions, merely words. They do not correspond with the facts of life.

What UNITROL Is

The fact is that mind and body are structurally and functionally a single unit; thus, the first part of the word UNITROL—**unit**. This obviously refers to the indivisible mind-body that **you** (your spirit, character or personality, if you wish) occupy.

The second part of the word UNITROL comes from the second syllable of the word **control**; thus—**control of the mind-body unit**. That is UNITROL.

In these chapters I will show you what UNITROL can do for you. I will show you simple techniques for the rapid development of UNITROL which will enable you to control most of the functions of your body, functions now altogether out of your conscious control.

The Miracle of
Voluntary Muscle Control

Bend your index finger as if you were beckoning someone to come to you. Now straighten it. This seems like a simple command and a simple performance. Yet, properly understood, this apparent simplicity is a very great and wonderful complexity.

In order to bend your little finger, you had to use your eyes to read the command on this page. You then had to send the message from the control center in your brain down the spinal cord and out along the nerves of the arm to the muscles of the little finger. This message was translated by the muscles receiving it so that some of them contracted when the finger bent, while other muscles relaxed. When the finger straightened, the muscles on the outer surface contracted and the muscles on the inner surface relaxed.

But that is not all. There had to be close coordination between bones, joints and blood vessels, as well as the muscles and nerve structures, in order to accomplish this apparently simple bending and straightening of your little finger.

The muscles involved are called voluntary muscles. These are the skeletal muscles, muscles attached to bones and joints. You can move these muscles on command from your own brain.

Most of us are tense and anxious practically all the time. We live in an atmosphere of world tension and anxiety—an age of speed and H-bombs and constant struggle.

I could go on to enumerate hundreds of causes for our general anxiety. You know very well the sources of your own individual anxiety. The point I wish to make is that such anxiety causes tension of the skeletal muscles.

This tension in turn increases our emotional tension. Notice the constant, restless movement of skeletal muscles in the individual under tension. The young father waiting for his baby to be born paces the floor, wrings his hands, chain-smokes one cigarette after another. Notice the restless motion of any individual under tension, the pointless movement of the hands, crossing or uncrossing of the legs, twiddling of thumbs, or involuntary spasm of muscles of the eye, face or neck—movements we know as tics.

Anxiety causes tension of the skeletal muscles and, like a vicious circle, tension in the skeletal muscles increases anxiety. Glandular secretions such as adrenalin pour into the bloodstream during such emotional and skeletal muscle tension, with a resultant increase in rate of the heartbeat and sometimes with elevation of blood pressure.

You Can Break
the Tension Chain

Now then, stop and think! You control these skeletal muscles. They are voluntary muscles. What would you give to be able to control these muscles so that when you are under tension, you could—on command—cause them to relax instantly? What would you give if you knew that such relaxation would instantly decrease your emotional tensions? There are times when you would give everything you possess, for it might be worth your life to have such control.

For example, if you already have a tendency to high blood pressure and are thrust into a situation of great tension and anxiety, the extra added push given to your blood pressure by skeletal muscle tension might be just enough to rupture an artery in your brain, producing a **stroke**. This might very well cost you your life. Now you can see why I say that you would give all you possess to prevent such an event.

You do not need to give all you possess. You need only read these chapters and apply them. You will then develop the simplest form of UNITROL—control of the skeletal muscles. The same muscles that you commanded to bend your index finger and straighten it are the muscles I am talking about. Such control is simple indeed when your learn UNITROL.

But UNITROL goes beyond teaching control of the voluntary skeletal muscles of the body.

Understanding How
Your Involuntary Muscles Work

There are other muscles in the body called involuntary muscles. Some of these are the muscles in the walls of the tubes that carry the blood supply of the body—the arteries. Spasm of one of these arteries, particularly an artery in the brain or the heart, may cause serious illness, chronic disability, or death.

Spasm of an artery of the brain may cause a small stroke. It has been truly said that death takes little bites. Each of these small strokes is a little death bite. Spasms of the arteries that bring blood to the heart (the coronary arteries) cause disabling chest pain—angina pectoris. If this spasm is severe, a coronary occlusion may result, with death of part of the heart muscle. This is the worst type of heart attack and may cause instant death.

Other involuntary muscles are the smooth muscles lining the intestinal tract. Spasm of the muscles of the lower end of the esophagus (the tube leading from mouth to stomach) may cause pain and may ultimately result in an ulcer of the esophagus. Spasm of the muscles at the outlet of the stomach (the pylorus) may cause retention of food and acids in the stomach far beyond the time they should remain in that organ. The resultant excess acid remaining in the stomach may partially digest the stomach lining itself, causing a peptic ulcer. The ultimate result of such an ulcer may be perforation with peritonitis, or hemorrhage and death. Spasm of smooth muscles in the large bowel (the colon) may cause constipation, abdominal pains, colitis in one form or another. Spasm of muscles near the outlet of the rectum may result in a difficult bowel movement, tearing the rectal outlet, with ulcer formation, hemorrhoids, etc.

These muscles are called involuntary because they are said to be out of voluntary control. Under ordinary circumstances you cannot command the arteries of your heart to relax, you cannot slow your heartbeat, you cannot command the arteries of your brain to relax, nor can you command the spasm in your intestines to go away. I have said **under ordinary circumstances.**

How UNITROL Gives You Command
of All Your Muscles

UNITROL changes all that. When you have become proficient in UNITROL, you will be able to slow your heart rate on command. You will be able to relax spastic muscles in the intestinal tract instantly. You will be able to lower your blood pressure rapidly. You will have some degree of control over these involuntary muscles. The degree of control you attain will depend upon the degree of practice that you give to UNITROL.

This seems like a fantastic promise. However, I can tell you from my own experience and from the experience of my patients that it is not at all fantastic; it is realistic, down-to-earth and practical. It is yours for the taking.

I will go still further. If you are aging more rapidly than you should be, it may very well be due to excess stress and anxiety, reflecting itself in the skeletal and smooth muscles of your body, and through them in the bones, joints, arteries, and intestinal tract. This muscle spasm in turn intensifies emotional stress and strain, and this further increases voluntary and involuntary muscle spasm. UNITROL breaks this vicious cycle. Relaxation of the muscles of your forehead and scalp and face erases the worry lines that now age your appearance. Relaxation of the skeletal and smooth muscles of the rest of your body will improve the blood supply to these muscles, and the blood supply to the bones and joints, thus releasing you from the bondage of stiff muscles and joints (some forms of arthritis) and brittle bones.

Relaxation of your heart artery muscles may release you from heart pain and the limitation of your activity resulting from such heart pain.

Relaxation of your intestinal tract muscles will result in better intestinal tract function, better digestion of your food, and better utilization of all food values. This in turn will have a rejuvenating effect upon the entire body, inasmuch as we truly are what we eat.

The total sum of relaxation will ease tensions in your mind to the point where you will achieve some measure of peace of mind where before there had been only tension, anxiety, stress and perhaps high blood pressure—a mental and emotional volcano.

The result of such release from tension throughout your entire mind and body very often reverses or halts the aging process. UNITROL is a veritable fountain of youth within yourself. That is where it always has been, and Ponce de Leon need not have sought beyond himself if he had only known UNITROL.

Are you overweight? If you are, it is probably due to the fact that you are consciously or unconsciously under emotional strain, and overeat in consequence. It is possible to release yourself from the bondage of your emotional tensions. When you are released you no longer need to overeat, and the excess weight melts away without difficult diets or dangerous drugs.

How Psychosomatic Illness
Affects Your Mind-Body Unit

In one of my books I have stated, "all disease is psychosomatic." This includes cancer. It includes all the allergies. It includes the so-called "organic" diseases of all kinds. Why? Very simply, because of our first statement relating to the indivisibility of mind and body. Mind and body function together as a unit. They **are** a unit. The division is a verbal one, arbitrary and contrary to fact. Therefore, even cancer has emotional components, as does every organic (somatic) disease. Remember that the disease affects Mr. Jones or Mrs. Smith, and not a "body" or a "mind" in a vacuum. It affects a real living person, a personality in an environment. Your physician must treat not only the body, but also the mind, the internal and the external environments of the patient. UNITROL takes this into account. UNITROL teaches you how to control the mind-body unit in its environment.

What does this mean in practical terms? What can it really

do for you? The answer is obvious. If you are suffering from high blood pressure, heart disease, allergy, obesity or even cancer, UNITROL can completely or partially release you from the bondage to drugs that you now use for pain, restore some measure of confidence and pleasure in living, lower your pressure, release muscle spasm in your arteries, restore mental and physical equilibrium, make you younger, prolong your life. That is the promise and the fulfillment of UNITROL.

Learn How to Throw Away Your Tranquilizers With UNITROL

When we remember that at least 90 per cent of all patients who enter a physician's office have functional disturbances—when we remember that these patients need reassurance more than drugs—and when we realize that UNITROL can control or eliminate the problem symptoms, the importance of UNITROL is obvious. When we realize that billions of dollars' worth of tranquilizers have been sold and will be sold, the need for a simple mind-body control therapy is obvious. The proper application of UNITROL will make tranquilizers generally obsolete.

However, you must first see your physician and be certain that your condition is functional and not organic. You may require specific drugs such as insulin for diabetes, or specific surgery. You cannot make your own diagnosis. Do not use UNITROL to replace your family physician. But you may use UNITROL directly, or under his supervision, with beneficial results in all cases, regardless of the diagnosis.

With UNITROL you will be on your way towards peace of mind, strength of body, renewal of youth, extension of life. You will be on your way to a healthier, happier, longer life with UNITROL.

UNITROL is More Than Muscle Control

However, there is much more to UNITROL than merely control of voluntary or involuntary muscles. There is control of thinking, control of attitudes, control of belief. If you could develop this control to its ultimate, you might be able to perform within yourself the same type of miracles that have been seen occasionally at Lourdes. Even cure of cancer might be possible. However, let me caution you that such instantaneous cures—even at Lourdes, where faith is very deep and intense, and the environment is absolutely perfect for such cures—are very rare.

How to Unleash
Your Secret Inner Power

As I have already indicated, UNITROL offers simple, workable methods that you can readily use yourself for the control of your body-mind unit. But UNITROL goes still further, and offers control of your body-mind unit through your spirit.

A human being consists of more than a body and its component parts. There are certain built-in reactions in all of us, peculiarities resulting from the reaction of your body-mind to its environment. But the whole is still greater than the sum of its parts, and there is an indefinable something within each of us—the spirit. I would go still further and say that this spirit is indestructible and immortal. It is part of God. Indeed, you can say, with justification, that God dwells within you. In that sense, **you are God.** If this is true, then the powers of God, His omnipotence and omniscience, are your powers.

This is a startling statement. It means that you have the power to control your destiny, the power of God within you. You can make yourself ill or you can produce good health at will. You can lengthen your life or shorten it. You can make

yourself old before your time or you can rejuvenate yourself
—exactly as you wish. There are no limitations to the powers
of God, and insofar as you believe that God dwells within you,
and that His powers are your powers, **there are no limitations
to your powers.**

UNITROL takes spirit into account, and when I say that
you control your mind-body unit, the **you** is your spirit, the
power of God within you, your personality structure if you
will.

As I have already indicated, we must work through the
power of God if we are to achieve maximum results with UNI-
TROL. It is important to realize that when there is a conflict
between your will and your emotions, your emotions will always win. For example, if you say to yourself, "I want to get
rid of this pain, but I don't feel that I can do it," rest assured
that you will not get rid of pain. Your **feeling** always wins
out over your **thinking.** You must have **faith,** you must believe,
you must implant your positive suggestions **on the emotional
level** if they are to be fully effective.

This is best accomplished by placing your positive suggestions at the emotional level of the God-power within you.
**If you make God your partner, nothing will be impossible
for you.** It is indeed true that if you have faith, "even as a
grain of mustard seed," nothing will be impossible unto you.
Your faith will literally move the mountains of care and
despair, anxiety and disease. How right Lincoln was when he
said, "It is difficult to make a man miserable while he feels he
is worthy of himself and claims kindred to the great God who
made him."

So, in UNITROL we utilize the spirit together with mind
and body as an indivisible unit. Remember that division of
these elements is arbitrary and only on a verbal level. Actually, nowhere in the body can you isolate mind, body, or spirit.
All exist together, as an indivisible unit. From this point on,
the all-powerful spirit of God will be working within you and
with you to develop your full capacity of UNITROL.

The Healing Force
of Your God-power

It is important for each of us who believes in God, the Divine
Intelligence in the universe, to realize the fact that the power
of God is within him. The Bible correctly states, "The Kingdom of Heaven is within you." Since the Kingdom of Heaven
is within you, and God resides in his Kingdom, **the powers
of God are within you.** They are yours to use.

When you do not use these powers, when you deny them
by denying your faith in yourself—by your negative attitudes,
your lack of confidence, your feeling of inferiority—this self-
denial is really a denial of God. Every pain in your body,
every diseased cell, tissue or organ, is a voluntary destruction
of the temple of God. It is a denial of the fact that the all-
powerful, all-wise God dwells within your body.

UNITROL not only removes symptoms directly by removing
voluntary and smooth muscle spasms, and by rooting out
negative attitudes and thoughts in your mind, but it also re-
places these negative attitudes and ideas by positive affirmations, positive beliefs, a strong and abiding faith in yourself
and in the God-power within you. This is a major strength of
UNITROL. UNITROL is the first medical and self-help technique to combine such positive replacement therapy with direct symptom removal therapy. Still further, UNITROL will
teach you how to uncover and remove the emotional dynamite
of your past, now repressed and buried in your subconscious
mind. You will note the power of your thoughts, your words.
You will put your energy in harmony with your God-power
and through the miracle of your mind you will take long steps
toward integrating the mind-body unit. You will learn to control the body, to unite mind and body, and launch yourself
on a new, full life. You must only remember that by using
your God-power through your body-mind unit, no goal is out
of reach.

To Sum It Up . . .

A few major points to remember:
1. UNITROL means **control** of the mind-body unit.
2. You **can** control both your voluntary and involuntary muscles.
3. If you unleash the God-Power within, nothing is impossible.

With UNITROL, you can overcome tension, worry, fear, anxiety, psychosomatic illness. Now let us begin your journey towards a newer, richer life.

chapter 2

How To Make Words Work as Your Own Magic Healers

The words you have heard and spoken throughout a lifetime are of tremendous importance. Every word you have heard, every sight, every sound, in short, every **sensation** that you have experienced from the time you were born to the present is recorded in your nervous system. As I have often said, sticks and stones may break your bones, but words can destroy you completely.

The words and sensations of an emotionally disturbing situation in your past may continue to act with great power to your detriment throughout a lifetime. They may at this moment be producing serious symptoms, grave tissue changes, and perhaps even paving the way for a fatal outcome. Yes, words can literally kill.

And so it is obviously important that we study our reactions to words and symbols, as well as our reactions to every sensation that we experience. Such study will disclose special corrective methods, as you will see.

Learn To Work With Your Nervous System

First, let me tell you a little about the structure and function of your nervous system. Then, we can study the response of your nervous system and your entire body to words and

33

symbols. You have already learned something about the great gap between words and the facts they represent. You will learn now how to evaluate words and your reactions to them. You need not know all the details about your nervous system anatomy. You need merely know that there is a part of the brain called the thalamus, and another part called the cortex. The thalamus (more correctly the hypothalamus) is the emotional zone, or "feeling" region. The cortex is the intelligence zone, or the "thinking" region.

There is a constant flow of electrical nerve impulses in both directions between the brain's cortex and its thalamus. The brain functions twenty-four hours a day, even while we sleep. The subconscious level of the brain never sleeps.

A healthy reaction to words, or to any stimulus, should involve both your thalamus and your cortex. Remember the simple admonition to count to ten before reacting when you are angry. There is good reason for this. Delay before reacting to any disturbing stimulus gives the cortex a chance to evaluate impulses from the thalamus. In simpler language, this delay gives the thinking region of your brain a chance to consider the possibilities of action when you are emotionally disturbed.

Your reactions should therefore be delayed until the impulse has passed to the thalamus first, to the cortex second, and then returned to the thalamus. Fools do indeed rush in where angels fear to tread.

Keep Your Head
and Keep Your Health

Most lower animals behave by responding in an undelayed fashion, by reflex action. In other words, there is no control by the intelligence zone. Reaction is rapid and unconsidered.

But you are a human being, and you have a thinking region in your brain. This makes you different from most animals in that opportunity is provided for consideration and "thinking" before reacting.

It must be obvious to you that emotional, undifferentiated and unthinking behavior will be harmful. You are not a monkey, but a man. Undelayed, emotional reactions may be suitable for most animals, and they may be acceptable for children in whom the intelligence zone of the brain is not yet fully developed. However, it is certainly undesirable for an adult human being to react in the same fashion as an animal or an infant.

Now you have a yardstick to measure your own emotional development and control. Do you fly off the handle easily? If you do, you are acting in a lower animal fashion. Your reactions are undelayed, thalamic in origin, emotional, animal-like. Are you calm and controlled? Do you deliberate before passing judgment? If so, your reactions are on the human level and you are using your thinking region as God intended.

Why is this so very important in our consideration of psychosomatic disease? Obviously, every time you react at an emotional level—without thinking—you send powerful impulses throughout your entire body. These impulses of uncontrolled or violent reactions—reactions of fear, anxiety, grief, rage—cause an outpouring of very powerful glandular secretions into your blood stream. If this goes on day after day, week after week, month after month, year after year, profound tissue changes take place. These tissue changes may be very damaging, and may actually shorten your life.

What Words Can Do To You

Let me give you a simple example to illustrate the fact that your entire body responds to words and symbols. If the word **fire** is shouted when you are sitting in a crowded theater, your reaction will most likely be undelayed—a panic response. You will experience fear, you may tremble and feel your heart pounding violently. Your mouth may be dry. You may experience a sensation of hollowness in your stomach. Your blood pressure will either rise or fall. Your face may turn white. Your legs and arms may feel weak and helpless. In this paralysis of fear action may be impossible.

Now stop and think. To what did your entire body react with such violence, such profound changes? Your body reacted in response to a single word, the word **fire**. You did not see the fire. There may have been no fire. Your reaction was to the word. There can be no question in your mind now that words by themselves do produce changes in your body. These changes may be harmful or they may be beneficial.

However, words are not the things they represent. For example, the word **steak** cannot be eaten. The word **chair** cannot be sat upon. In the example of the shouting of the word **fire** in the theater, obviously the word **fire** is not actually fire. And yet you reacted as though you were already enveloped or surrounded by flames. You did not see any flames. You did not feel the warmth of the fire, you experienced no pain. Your reaction was to the word.

Obviously, then, the word is not the thing represented. And this is true of all words. It seems very obvious, but it is not so apparent unless you think about it.

It would be a healthy reaction if nervous system impulses produced by words were given an opportunity to pass through the thinking region of your brain before you reacted. In the example given above, if it had passed through your thinking region you would have reacted quite differently.

You would have looked about to see if there was actually a fire. You would have observed where the fire was located, so that you might choose your course of action more intelligently. You would have looked for the nearest exit. You might then have decided to sit still and avoid the panic of others. You might reason that you could walk calmly to the nearest exit and escape. Whatever your decision might have been, it would have been reached as the result of a delayed reaction, the impulse passing through the thinking region of the brain before you reacted.

However, when you think of words as things (as most of us do), the word **fire** is the fire. Your reaction is then on a thalamic animal level.

Therefore, words and situations must be checked carefully by the thinking region of your brain before you react. Otherwise, you will be reacting to the word rather than the actual facts.

How Words Affect Your Health

Let me emphasize for you still further the fact that words have meanings far beyond the meanings given to them in the most extensive dictionary. Thus, they have no "general meaning," in spite of the dictionary. Remember, dictionaries are merely words about words. We are considering words as they affect our nervous system, and our entire bodies. We are considering our health and our life.

For instance, when you are not feeling too well, or when you **think** you might be ill, you are apt to say to yourself, "I am sick." Simple words, aren't they? However, their power can drive people into the depths of despair and disease. As soon as you say "I am sick," your subconscious mind receives the message and your entire system responds with a letdown. This letdown may be first felt as lethargy, as depression, and if you can **feel** this way, you can imagine what is happening to the cells, organs, and systems within you. They too get depressed. That is, their normal function is interfered with, and when this happens, the individual is on the road to true illness or a more serious ailment than he or she ought to have. What you believe, what you think, more than any of us realize, actually **is** so—or soon can be.

Don't Trick Yourself

Consider the old and somewhat sadistic trick which you may have been subjected to yourself. In this "stunt," several people, in turn, after arranging details in advance, walk up to an individual and tell him that he looks sick. After three or four of these not so cheerful messages, the individual most often begins to actually feel sick, or at least a bit under the weather, and once the suggestion is planted, there is no telling how far this "sick feeling" may go. So you see, words and thoughts often do control the way you feel. Once you recognize this, you will have made great progress toward improving your mental and physical health. You must always verify feelings and thoughts in terms of what **really** is. If you do not feel up to par, examine your state of health or see your physician in order to get at the truth of the matter. Or, if you are subjected to something like the "trick" mentioned above, simply reflect on how you really feel, instead of reacting to the gloomy words of other people as though they were true. You simply need to stick to the "facts," and you will not get lost inside yourself.

How To Make Words
Work for You with UNITROL

In terms of physical and mental health, you must realize that words can influence your emotions, and in the emotions, disease processes can originate. Let us take the word **love**. This word can cause great damage to the emotional and consequently the physical life of any individual. We agree that love is essential for normal human development, but what does love mean?

The word **love** has many meanings. It will be clear that the meaning of the word **love** to you can never be the same as the meaning of the word love to anyone else. **All meanings are individual.**

To an infant, love means proper feeding, and perhaps proper care of toilet functions. If the infant is given a bottle or a breast at regular intervals as he becomes hungry and is cleaned when he moves his bowel or urinates, then he is said to be given love. That is a perfectly proper meaning of the word at that age.

The word **love** begins to include fondling, kissing, caressing, and recognition of accomplishment. At a still later stage in life, love begins to involve the sex organs.

But what does love mean to the adult? Here again we find many shades of meaning, and many interpretations. And we observe, as we have with other words, that the meanings are highly individual and never the same for another person. To one person, **love** means the provision of a home and the opportunity to sleep with someone of the opposite sex. To another, **love** means a daily kiss before leaving for the office, flowers on anniversaries, and perhaps an occasional box of candy. To still another person, **love** means mink coats and diamonds. And so on, ad infinitum.

It will be obvious to you that if your wife considers love to mean candy and flowers and a card on each anniversary, and if you do not provide these symbols, she will say that you no longer love her. In your own mind, perhaps, you feel that you love your wife very much. However, your love does not mean flowers and candy or an anniversary card. You can see no reason for your wife to go home to mother. And yet she may.

Now that you are more fully aware of the significance of language, the individual meanings of words, and the many levels at which words and objects may be observed, you will be less likely to react on a purely thalamic, emotional, undelayed basis. You will evaluate more accurately, you will be more understanding, you will realize the problems in communicating your thoughts and ideas to someone else, and you will be better equipped to love.

Think Twice and Save Your Life

Let us suppose that a doctor tells the patient that he has "colitis." The delayed reaction, passing the word through the thinking region of the brain for analysis, is obviously better than being thrown into a panic of anxiety and fear. The patient might think to himself, "colitis means literally an inflammation of the colon. There are many forms of colitis. The inflammation may be temporary or it may be chronic. It may be curable or it may be incurable. It may be due to emotions, or it may be due to bacteria. Indeed, for all I know, it may be due to many other causes. It may be limited to one little part of the colon, or it may involve the entire bowel. There are many facts that I honestly must know about this word 'colitis.' I must ask the doctor to explain the facts."

The patient who thinks this way would then ask for further details. He would want to know the levels of observation. How was the diagnosis reached? Did the doctor see the inflammation in the colon? Where was it located? How much of the colon is involved? What is the cause of the inflammation? Is it curable?

Obviously, this is a sane, logical, cortical-thalamic reaction. That patient will not be thrown into a panic. The word "colitis" has lost its danger. The patient has used his thinking level.

How different the picture might be if the patient were not trained in adequate reaction to words. When the doctor says "colitis," panic grips the patient. Fear, terror, and all the physical accompaniments of such panic might result. His heart begins to pound, he begins to tremble, his mouth becomes dry, there is a sense of impending disaster or death. He pictures cancer. This is the emotional, thalamic level of reaction. It is an animal, infantile, immature level of reaction.

The safety device offered by delayed reactions is obviously very important. There are other safety devices that can be built into your nervous system. One of these is called **indexing**.

How to Use the Indexing Technique and Escape Anxiety

Indexing teaches you that no two things are alike. Everything is individual, and appears different to the next fellow. No two people are identical. No two problems are identical. Cancer in one person is not cancer in another. Your Aunt Mary's colitis is not your colitis.

Aunt Mary might actually have died of colitis, but that does not mean you will die of colitis. "Colitis" is a word, and the disease Aunt Mary had was not a word, but a unique fact relating only to herself and her colon. It has no connection whatsoever with the fact of your disease in your colon. Every colitis in the world is a personal matter—individual and unique. This is true even though yours may have been caused by a similar organism to that which caused Aunt Mary's colitis.

Even cancer is unique and individual. One person with cancer of the colon may die within a few months. Another may live for many years. In a third, the disease will spontaneously disappear. You must be aware of generalizations and inaccurate evaluations. You must habitually distrust generalizations, and think of colitis number **one** (Aunt Mary's), colitis number **two** (yours), colitis number **three** (Mr. Smith's), and so on—ALL of them individual.

In this way, you can **index** people, things, incidents, **and** diseases and thereby put each one in its proper place. You will see that each incident, each disease, is sufficient unto itself, and though a word like "colitis" may be used to speak of an illness in general, all the people who have the disease have individual and unique cases, depending upon their mental and physical condition.

By breaking up your response to incidents in this way, and by applying sound reasoning, you will be able to better evaluate the events that make up your reality, and you will no longer suffer the anxiety that comes from relating one event to another, more serious, event. You will be free to see everything that happens in a new light—the light of reason and full understanding. Now is the time to reassert your individuality by reacting to people and events as they specifically relate to you. The key to this healthy individuality and reason is **indexing**.

How to Use the Dating Technique
to Really See and Understand Yourself Now

Another important safety device is **dating**. If everything is given a date, we realize that the world is in a state of continual change. Thus, if you bought an apple yesterday, it is not the same apple today; certain chemical changes have taken place in it. You might say it is becoming rotten in spots today. It wasn't rotten yesterday. It is a different apple today.

The same thing may be said for you. You aren't the same person today that you were yesterday. Cellular, organic, and psychological changes have occurred which make you a different person. Even if you don't feel the changes each day, they are there.

We spoke of **love** as changing at different levels of life. The **love** of infancy is not the **love** of adolescence, nor is the **love** of adolescence the **love** of adult life. The **love** of your honeymoon is not the **love** of your tenth or twentieth anniversary. Thus, the word **love** has different meanings with regard to dates. Everything has meaning only in relation to dates. There is constant change in all of life.

Learn to put a date on everything that has happened to you, every bitter frustration, every failure, every emotional disturbance of your lifetime. When you have learned to date these events, these disturbances, you can then file them in your memory and see them in proper perspective. They did not happen to **you**; they happened to the person you **were** at the time. **You** are no longer that person. Everything changes, and when you learn to date disturbing events in your life, you can then go on to a more productive life in the future without this heavy burden.

To illustrate the safety devices of indexing and dating let us assume that you "hate" your mother. Whom and what do you actually hate? It may be that you hate a generalization—the term **mother**. Hate is a harmful and destructive emotion, and if you **must** hate, let it not be generalizations! Direct your hate against a specific individual or a specific cause.

You don't hate the generalization **mother**, but your own mother. Now go a step further and find out how it was that **mother** hurt you, and when. You may recall an injury done to you by **mother** twenty or thirty years ago. Now you have placed a date on the injury. Dating has a beneficial effect. Twenty or thirty years ago your mother was a very different person, and so were you. It becomes very immature to carry a hatred for any individual for twenty or thirty years.

It becomes doubly immature when you realize that your life is being disturbed by a hatred for something that occurred twenty or thirty years before. Once this becomes clear, you will no longer hate. You will have analyzed away your hatred, using the safety devices of indexing and dating.

Now, make a list of all the things in your life that upset you. Go over this list carefully. See how many of them are actually dated and need **dating**. After you have dated those things which are no longer valid for the present **you**, you will have taken a very big step toward renewed mental and physical health. You will "see" people and events as they are right NOW.

To Sum It Up . . .

This has been a most important chapter for you:

1. You have learned to delay your reactions, particularly in emotionally charged situations. From now on you will not react in a rapid, animal, emotional fashion. You will first pass the problem through the thinking region of your brain, and you will afterward act in a calm and controlled fashion. This will protect your mind and body from violent disturbances.

2. You have learned that words are not things, and you will stop reacting to labels as if they were things. You will realize that there are as many meanings for words as there are people who hear and use those words.

3. You have learned not to react to your doctor's diagnosis of your condition as if it represented the same disease that carried off your uncle, aunt, father, mother, or friend. The word he used is merely a label, a general label with very little meaning. Your disease is different, unique; it never has and never will be duplicated anywhere in the world.

4. You have learned to put a date on all the disturbing episodes of your past, so you can truly "see" these disturbances as of that date. Everything changes. You have changed. You have dated the old, and are now prepared to go on hopefully and optimistically into the future.

5. UNITROL has begun to alter your nervous system, and the reactions of your nervous system. From this point on, and forever more, you will be calmer, happier, healthier. You will live in the present, and not in the past.

chapter 3

Now that you have
a better understanding
of language and its ef-
fect on you, you are

Using The Key Word Technique For Health Control

ready to apply an important phase of UNITROL, voluntary
muscle control.

Like all profound truths, this truth that you can and
should control your voluntary muscles and not let them control you is very simple. Yet, it has been overlooked for gen-
erations—indeed, for centuries. There is no doubt in my mind
that if we learned full control of our voluntary muscles, and
went no further in UNITROL (although there is much further to go), a tremendous percentage of our emotional disturbances would disappear. We would attain a large measure
of tranquility and peace of mind. Our harried, ceaseless,
pointless, thoughtless activity would come to an abrupt end,
and many of our superficial neuroses and their associated
physical symptoms would be cleared up.

How to Feel Tension in Your Muscles

The first step is to learn the difference between a tense,
contracted muscle and a relaxed muscle. Let us start with
the muscles around the eye socket. Close your eyes gently.
This requires merely lowering the eyelids. Now tighten all the
muscles around the eye (the eye socket muscles), as if you

45

were squinting with your eyes closed. Feel the tension in these muscles. Put your fingers on these muscles and you will feel them tighten. You will feel the wrinkle lines forming at the outer margin of the eye socket and underneath the eyes. These tension lines, these worry lines, become the lines of aging as time passes. By avoiding muscle tension in this region you can literally rejuvenate your face, and once more regain the skin of youth around your eyes. You can prevent rapid future aging of your face.

How to Recognize a Relaxed Muscle

Now relax your eye socket muscles. You now know the difference between tension and relaxation in a muscle. You have felt the difference within yourself and with your fingers. Now do the same with the muscles of your forehead. Tighten your forehead muscles. You can feel the tightness. You can feel it even in your eyes, because such tightening of the forehead muscles is usually associated—practically automatically—with tightening of the eye socket muscles.

Now relax these muscles. See how much better you feel when they are relaxed. When you tighten them you may feel a mild aching sensation in your forehead or in your eyes. When you relax them the aching sensation disappears instantly.

Finding Tension in
Your Forehead and Cheek Muscles

Now place the palm of your hand gently upon your forehead and tighten the muscles again. You can feel the muscles tighten, the brows pull together, the worry lines appearing between the eyebrows at the root of the nose. Now relax these muscles. You can feel them actually smoothing out under your hand.

If you have a headache, just placing the palm of your hand gently against your forehead helps to relax these muscles, and the headache often melts away. If the ache is in the eyes as well, place the palms of your hands gently over both eyes, with the fingers of the left hand above the left eye, and the fingers of the right hand above the right eye. You will feel the muscles relax, the tension ease, and the ache slip away.

Now you know the feeling of tension and relaxation in the muscles of the forehead and around the eyes.

Do the same with the muscles of your cheeks. When you tense these muscles, your lips will be drawn upward into the grimace of a smile. Now relax your cheek muscles. When you do this the grin disappears and the cheeks become smooth again. Now repeat this movement, placing your hand over the tightening and relaxing cheek muscles. Feel the bunching up of the muscles of the cheeks when they are contracted, and the softness and flexibility of the muscles under your finger tips when they are relaxed. Generally speaking, it is the soft, flexible muscle that is our goal.

Now purse your lips as if you were going to blow air through them. You are contracting the muscles of your lips when you do that. Get the feeling of tightness when they are contracted. Notice that it is a tense feeling. Now relax your lips. The feeling of relaxation is calming, and puts you at ease.

You **must** learn this difference before you can proceed with UNITROL. It is basic to your development in self-control to know the feeling of a tense muscle and the feeling of a relaxed muscle. **Relaxation is your objective.**

How Voluntary Muscle Tension
Affects Your Emotions

Control of the muscles of the eyes, the forehead and the face are essential to relaxation. Impulses from this area reach the brain rapidly, and emotions are reflected in your face almost

before any other part of the body. Remember, the face re-
flects the emotions of an actor better than any other part of
the body.

When you are unhappy, you frown. The corners of your
mouth begin to droop and your lips may purse. Your eye
socket muscles contract, and you may cry. If you cry, your
cheek muscles contract and the contraction may be very violent
and unpleasant.

These physical contractions of the eye muscles, frowning
with the forehead muscles, contraction of the cheek muscles,
each in turn increase your feeling of sadness and intensify and
prolong your associated depression. This is a vicious cycle.
The emotional disturbance causes the muscle tension, and this
in turn increases the emotional disturbance—and around and
around we go, spinning into the vortex of a deep depression.

Try this simple experiment. Smile! Don't you feel better
when you do that? Of course you do. Your smile stimulates a
pleasant feeling, a pleasant attitude. No matter how bad you
feel at the time you smile, the smile makes you feel better.
Here you have a perfect example of an emotional attitude that
results from the action of voluntary muscles.

You can now see the importance of the face muscles. When
you have learned to relax the muscles of your eyes and eye
sockets, the muscles of your cheeks and lips and forehead,
and when you are skillful at such relaxation, you can produce
instant relaxation of the rest of your body by making facial
relaxation your first step. When you are unhappy, you can
practically reverse your unhappiness instantly—at least to
some degree—by smiling. Try that experiment the next time
you are upset. It will work wonders for you. And remember
the old adage: "Smile, and the world smiles with you; weep
and you weep alone." It is very, very true.

How to Relax for Health

Since you have been shown how tension in your muscles can affect your emotions, you realize how important it is to relax. Now I will show you, step by step, how to achieve this very important relaxation. Throughout this instruction I want you to think of me as your personal physician. Remember, I am at your side at all times, and I want you to hear my voice as you read these words, and know that my voice and my guidance are intended only for you. Look upon me as your guide. I will help you to overcome your anxieties, your tensions, your lack of confidence, your illnesses. And if you are under the care of your local physician, surgeon, or other medical consultant, for an organic ailment, no matter how serious, I will be by your side as well, working with you and with your consultants to help you overcome the psychosomatic components in your problem.

Now I want you to lie down on a bed. I want you to lie on your back, with your hands resting comfortably alongside your body, palms downward.

I want you to close your eyes.

I want you to relax the muscles around your eyes, and the muscles of your lips and cheeks and forehead.

Pause now and realize that you are completely relaxed, tranquil, calm, placid, without anxiety, without fear. You are completely at ease.

I want you now to relax the muscles around your shoulders, and let this relaxation move down your arms and forearms to your fingertips. Let every muscle in your shoulders, your arms, your forearms and your fingers go limp and loose. I want this relaxation to be complete.

Now I want you to take a deep breath, and as you gently let the air out I want the relaxation to deepen throughout your entire body. I want you to repeat the deep breath and the

deepening of relaxation as you exhale. Let this deepening relaxation spread down your entire body like a wave.

I want you to let the relaxation spread to the muscles of
your abdomen so that they become limp and loose.

Now let it spread to the muscles of your buttocks and your
thighs, your hips, down your legs to your toes. Let your legs
become completely loose, limp and relaxed.

Take another deep breath and let it out. As you let it out,
all your tensions and anxieties and worries will go out and
away, no longer a part of you.

Repeat the deep breath and exhalation of air, anxiety and
worries once again. As you do, you will find that every muscle goes into a state of even deeper relaxation, from your
scalp to your toes.

Relaxation will soon be so deep that you will be on the verge
of sleep. In a later chapter I will teach you how to produce
instant sleep, immediately following voluntary muscle relaxation.

That is the simple UNITROL technique for the basic first
phase of muscle-mind relaxation.

Although it may take you several minutes to learn this
technique now, I will soon show you how to achieve this state
of deep skeletal muscle relaxation instantly—on command. I
will show you how to achieve it whether you are sitting or
standing or lying down, and to whatever degree you wish.

Tension Testing and Relaxation

Now let us use the tension-testing and relaxation technique
to emphasize the difference between tension and relaxation,
and to heighten your sense of control and awareness of those
tensions and relaxations.

I want you to stand up and become fully alert and awake
once again, in your usual state of muscle tone. And now I want
you to lie down again, in the same position as before.

Now raise your head from the pillow and feel the tension in the muscles in the back of your neck. Now let your head drop back into a state of complete relaxation. Let it fall back limp and loose. There is still some tension in the muscles at the back of your neck. Feel it? Let it go. Let it go completely.

Now tighten the muscles in your face by drawing up the muscle around your eyes, tensing the muscles in your cheek and wrinkling your forehead. Feel the tension? Now relax suddenly and completely. Feel the difference, and let the depth of relaxation become more intense. Let your face muscles go completely.

Now tighten your fist. Let it go. You felt the tension, now feel the relaxation as it goes through your entire body.

Now flex your arm at the elbow, "to make a muscle" in the arm. Feel the tension. Now drop it, letting your arm fall limp and loose by your side. Feel the relaxation! Feel it now throughout the whole arm, throughout the shoulder, down to the fingers.

Now bend your legs up against your abdomen and feel the tension of the muscles in your thigh.

Bend your toes and feet up toward your head and feel the tension in the muscles of your legs and in your feet and toes.

Now let your legs fall down flat on the bed, completely relaxed and at ease. Feel the relaxation!

Now you have tested tension and relaxation throughout the muscles of the body. This is also an excellent technique to produce relaxation, moving from one muscle group to another, from tension to relaxation—until the entire body is fully relaxed.

UNITROL Basic Command Technique

However, you can more rapidly accomplish the same purpose by the UNITROL basic command technique, by commanding the muscles of your body to relax, group by group, from head to toe. Remember that you (the God-power within you) control every muscle, every organ, every tissue, every cell, every function of your body. Your muscles are your servants, and they will do exactly as you command.

Now that you know how relaxation feels as compared to tension, the simple command to any tense muscles of your body, from head to toe, will cause them to go into immediate relaxation, and your entire body will become limp, loose, relaxed and at ease.

When this occurs there will be no anxiety impulses coming from any of these muscles to your brain and nervous system. In consequence, your brain and nervous system will also be relaxed and at ease, at rest. Many of your superficial worries will drop away with full relaxation, and with the deep exhalations. You will find yourself fully relaxed physically and mentally, at peace with the world. You will find yourself in the first phase of UNITROL, the phase of UNITROL relaxation.

How to Achieve Key Word Control

Now, let us proceed to the specific Key Command Technique of UNITROL.

The principle of the key command technique is very simple indeed. It involves substituting a word, a phrase, or a mental picture for the entire set of instructions in the previous section. You may choose any word that you wish to represent the complete set of head to toe commands. The words I suggest are **UNITROL—Relax!** I prefer these words because you are not apt to hear such words spoken in general conversation, nor are you likely to read them in any book other than this. Therefore, you are not going to be predisposed to a state of relaxation at chance times when you may not desire it.

And now, I want you to do exactly as I say. Lie down and practice the voluntary muscle relaxation technique described previously. Relax yourself completely by repeating the command phrases for each group of muscles from head to toes. Enjoy this state of relaxation for ten to 15 minutes, or longer if you wish. If you find yourself going off to sleep, do not allow it to happen at this time.

After you have enjoyed this state of relaxation, I want you to rouse yourself from relaxation by saying, "My muscles will now return to a normal state of tone, and I will feel wonderful—rested, relaxed, rejuvenated." You are then to stand up.

Walk about a little. Now lie down again.

The Secret of Depth Relaxation

Relax and close your eyes.

This time, merely say to yourself, or aloud, "UNITROL—RELAX!" You will feel yourself going into a deeper and deeper state of relaxation. You feel wonderful. It is as if you were floating, light as a feather, effortlessly, and you are content to let yourself drift off into a deeper and deeper state of relaxation.

It is a wonderful feeling. Now go deeper; relax your muscles even more. As your muscles relax, all tension and anxiety drop away. All worries disappear. You are at peace with the world. You no longer care about anything. You have attained relaxation of mind and body to a degree that you never before dreamed possible.

Tell yourself that when you awaken from the state of relaxation, you will feel wonderful. You will be relaxed, at ease for the rest of the day, and as long thereafter as you wish. You will be vital, alert, alive, active, and happy. You will be content and carefree. Problems that seemed insurmountable to you before will now be solved easily. If your problems cannot be solved you will learn to accept the inevitable gracefully. You will learn to live with situations that before seemed intolerable to you. You will be better adjusted in every way—

happier, healthier, and younger, every day in every way.

Now, as your state of relaxation becomes deeper, imagine a genie standing beside your bed. He says to you, "I am going to grant your unspoken wish. From now on, any time you wish to go into this state of deep relaxation, this deep state of peaceful, calm, quiet relaxation of mind and body, you will be able to do so by repeating the words **UNITROL—Relax**. When you say this, the relaxation of mind and body, the complete calm and peace that you are now enjoying, will appear instantly."

From now on, the words UNITROL—RELAX will represent the complete state of relaxation that you have just enjoyed, and all the command words that you used previously to produce that state of relaxation. From this point on you will go instantly into this state of relaxation every time you say the words, **UNITROL—Relax**! After you have again enjoyed this state of relaxation for 10 to 15 minutes, repeat the same awakening phrase used before, and you will stand up relaxed and refreshed. You will have never felt better in your life. That 10 or 15 minutes will be equivalent to hours of ordinary sleep.

Now, repeat the experience again, using the words **UNITROL—Relax**! as your key word command control phrase. The more often you repeat the experience, the better will be the response of your subconscious mind and your skeletal muscles. Remember the significance of repetition in making impressions upon the subconscious mind. Repetition is one of the major principles in the development of UNITROL therapy.

How to Relax—From the Neck Down

You may practice **UNITROL—Relax**! while sitting as well as when lying down. If you do it while sitting, you may prefer to develop relaxation only from the neck down. This is particularly effective while sitting in a theater and watching a motion picture or a stage show. It will give you wonderful relaxation, and you will leave the theater completely rested and tranquil. As I have already said, it is the equivalent of many hours of ordinary sleep.

However, when you use the technique while sitting in the theater, you will not want to close your eyes, and you will want to remain mentally alert so that you may enjoy the performance. To do this you merely alter the key words a little, and say, **UNITROL—Relax—from the neck down!** This will have the effect of producing complete relaxation, precisely as before, but this time only from the neck down.

You must practice UNITROL relaxation as often as possible. You can do it while sitting, to some degree while standing and walking, and always while lying down. The more often you practice, the better. Repetition is the keynote to success.

Each time that you place yourself in a state of UNITROL relaxation, you are not merely resting and bringing tranquility to your body and mind. In addition, you are strengthening the tissues of your body, and allowing the body-mind unit to renew itself, to rebuild itself, and so prepare you to better fight anxiety, disease, and the stress of daily living. UNITROL relaxation does indeed give you a new lease on life.

To Sum It Up . . .

This is a most important chapter, for in it you have learned how tension in your voluntary muscles affects your emotions, and how to find immediate release from tension through key word control.

Key word control works by:
1. Registering a specific command in the subconscious mind —where **nothing** is forgotten.
2. Associating the command, UNITROL—Relax, with the actual feeling of deep and peaceful relaxation.

Remember, as in most things, practice makes perfect. Repeat the exercises in this chapter until you have mastered voluntary muscle relaxation completely. Then you will have taken a giant step toward the mastery of UNITROL, toward freeing yourself from tension, towards a happier, healthier, **better** life.

Since the
subconscious
mind is be-
low the level

Unlock Your Subconscious Storehouse and Empty Your Problem Pockets

of consciousness, it does not seem possible that we can actually hold a conversation with this level of our mind. However, it can be done. In this chapter I will teach you how to
reach your subconscious mind.

First, let us review some of the characteristics of the subconscious mind. The subconscious mind is the ancient level
of the mind, in contrast with the more recent cortical, thinking level. The subconscious mind is the primitive, animal level
of the brain. As such, it controls major involuntary functions
of the body. Such functions as the rate of heartbeat, level of
blood pressure, secretion of the all important endocrine glands
—all functions outside of voluntary command—are to a large
extent directed by the subconscious mind. Obviously, the subconscious mind is of extreme importance. Obviously, also, it
would be a major accomplishment if we could reach the subconscious mind and actually determine its content. It would
be even more important if we could control this vital level
of the brain.

The Special Language
of Your Subconscious Mind

Inasmuch as the subconscious mind is a primitive animal mind, it accepts general commands best. It interprets all commands literally.

As an example of general commands being accepted more readily by the subconscious mind, we might consider the affirmation, "Every day, in every way, I am getting younger and younger, happier and happier, healthier and healthier." All statements given to the subconscious mind should be in general terms such as these. However, if specific commands are to be given to the subconscious mind, they should be combined with strong emotions. Emotional (feeling) motivations will give force to such specific commands, and the subconscious mind is more likely to act upon them.

How to Teach
Your Subconscious Mind

Another important characteristic of the subconscious mind is that it is particularly susceptible to repetition. We learn best by repetition. The subconscious mind is a recording mechanism. Think of it now as a gigantic record, each groove representing all the sensations of a particular incident. Now then, if you wish to emphasize any particular idea, experience or technique, it is best to deepen the grooves representing this idea, experience or technique. This deepening is attained by repetition.

It is precisely the same technique that you use when you want to memorize a poem. You repeat it over and over again, until it is firmly impressed upon your subconscious mind. When you have done that, the words return to you easily when you need them. It is simply a playback of the recording you have made yourself.

That is why it is so important for you to practice these techniques. Practice makes perfect impressions upon the subconscious mind and perfect playbacks when you need them.

Never Say If

Another interesting characteristic of the subconscious mind is that it will act best upon positive affirmations. Always be very positive and definite in everything you say to the subconscious mind. Do not use negative terms. Do not be uncertain. Do not say, for example, "I will **try** to relax." Never use the word **try**. Tell your subconscious mind that you **will** relax.

Never say **if**. For example, don't say, "It is time to relax **if** I can." Say, "I **can** relax. Relax now!" Remember that your subconscious mind is your servant. If you show any signs of doubt or uncertainty, your servant may take advantage of your attitude and not do his job well. Make your commands authoritative, make them literally correct by choosing the proper words, and do not have any doubt in your mind that your commands will be obeyed.

On the other hand, you may be gentle with your commands, if you wish. Precisely as you would with an obedient servant, you may say, "You may now relax completely." This is called a permissive command and is perfectly acceptable. Indeed, sometimes it is even more acceptable to the subconscious mind than an authoritative direct command. You will soon find out which type of command works best for your own subconscious mind. Once you have discovered this, use it regularly.

How to Tap the Power
of Your Subconscious

A major characteristic of the subconscious mind is its complete and unquestioning obedience when properly contacted. It will do precisely as you say. For example, it will put into

effect any repeated mental image presented to it over a prolonged period. If you are overweight, and will hold before
your subconscious mind the mental image of yourself as slimmer, healthier, happier and **sexually more attractive,** your
subconscious mind will make every effort to convert this image
into reality. Such an image, properly presented to the subconscious mind at frequent intervals and for prolonged time
periods, will melt away the pounds for you. You will soon be
precisely as slim as you picture yourself.

Remember that your subconscious mind can change or stop
sensation from any part of your body. If you are in pain, it
can stop the pain so that you are no longer aware of the painful stimulus, whether it be a broken bone or a heart attack.

Your subconscious mind can alter tissue reactions. It can
help you get rid of edema (swelling of tissues), such as that
resulting from a sprained ankle. It can help you get rid of the
swelling of tissues in the nose and eyes during an allergic
episode such as hay fever. It can alter tissue reactions in
asthma, so that the muscles of the bronchial tubes relax, excessive secretion stops and the asthma attack is ended.

Your subconscious mind can hasten or slow healing. It can
put you to sleep instantly, and can waken you at any pre-
arranged time.

Your subconscious mind never sleeps. A simple and obvious
illustration is the way a mother wakens when her child whim-
pers or cries in another room. She wakens from deep sleep at
the slightest sound from her child, although other noises do
not wake her.

There are two specific techniques for contacting your subconscious mind: the **pendulum method** and the **projection
method.**

How the Pendulum Technique
Tells You About Yourself

The pendulum method is very ancient, but the modern application of this method as a specific device for conversing with the subconscious was developed by Le Cron.*

The pendulum, as the name implies, is merely a small weight on a string, a thread or a chain. In my experience it is best that the weight be an object with strong personal emotional content. A wedding ring, a piece of jewelry of sentimental value, or any small object that you treasure for emotional reasons will be perfectly adequate.

If you have no such object on hand, I would suggest the use of a half dollar or a quarter. Money has strong emotional content for most of us, since we have been taught its value and significance from childhood.

If the object is a ring, it is a simple matter to tie a string approximately twelve inches long to one end of the ring. If it is an object that allows no room for tying, such as a coin, attach the string to the margin with scotch tape.

To put the pendulum into use, sit in front of a table and rest your elbow on the table. If you are right handed, you will use the right hand. If you are left handed, use the left.

Rest your elbow on the table in front of you. Hold the loose end of the string between your thumb and forefinger, and let the weighted end dangle over the table top.

And, now before we proceed, let me tell you something of the principle behind this technique. You have already observed, in our previous lessons, the close relationship between ideas and muscle actions. If you command your finger to bend, it will do so. If you command it to straighten, it will do that. If you tell your hand to clench into a fist, it will clench. These

* *Self-Hypnotism: The Technique and Its Use in Daily Living,* Prentice-Hall, 1964.

are examples of ideas translated into skeletal muscle action.

Unconscious ideas are similarly translated into skeletal muscle action. The unconscious mind is constantly sending impulses to the muscles of the body. Your unconscious mind will send impulses to the pendulum, through the muscles of the forearm and hand. Try it now, and think of the pendulum as swinging from left to right and back again in front of the body. Visualize this motion. In very short order you will notice that your unconscious mind has sent the necessary impulses to the muscles, and the pendulum begins to swing in front of you.

Now send a command to these muscles to change the direction and have it swing back and forth away from you, toward you, away from you, etc. You will notice that the pendulum will do precisely that in very short order. You are not conscious of the motions that make this possible. The thought has been translated into imperceptible muscle motions to produce this magnified movement of the weight at the end of the string.

Similarly, the pendulum can be consciously or unconsciously commanded to swing in a clockwise circle or a counterclockwise circle.

The pendulum can now become your point of contact with the subconscious mind. Let us allow a motion away from and back toward the body just as if you were nodding your head "yes"—to represent an affirmative **yes** answer. Let us agree that if the pendulum swings back and forth from left to right in front of the body just as if you were shaking your head from left to right to indicate "no," this will represent a negative **no** answer. Let us further assume that if the pendulum swings in a clockwise circle, this will represent an **"I don't know"** answer. And let us finally assume that if the pendulum swings in a counterclockwise direction that this represents an **"I won't tell"** answer.

It is important to realize that a simple "yes" or "no"

answer is not always possible. There are many shades of gray, and not just clear-cut white or black, clean-cut "yes" or "no." Therefore, it is important that you develop the projection technique (next chapter) to help you clarify the simple "yes" or "no" answers of the pendulum or finger motion methods.

We are now ready to converse with the subconscious. Have a set of specific questions ready to ask your subconscious, questions relating to a particular emotional or emotional-physical problem that may be troubling you. Write down these questions in a series on a piece of paper, and have the paper in front of you, together with a pen or pencil. Have two columns after each question, one headed "yes" the other headed "no." You are now prepared to check off "yes" or "no" in answer to each question, making a simple check mark with the pencil held in your other hand.

Although this technique will work in many cases even if you are completely alert, it will work best if you close off as many senses as possible, and if you are as completely relaxed as possible. In that state the subconscious mind is more available. It is more available because sensations do not occupy and distract the conscious mind, and it is more at rest. The subconscious mind can then take over more fully.

You must now say to yourself, UNITROL—Relax, or UNITROL—Relax—it is the will of God. You will, of course, go into an immediate state of voluntary muscle relaxation, and your mind will be stilled. You will be at peace, relaxed, completely at ease. Under these circumstances your subconscious mind can be easily contacted.

You may now open your eyes and ask the first question. The direction of the pendulum motion will be totally controlled by your subconscious, and the answers very often will be ones that you did not expect. However, they will be literal truth. Your subconscious mind knows the answers, and will not withhold the information.

For example, let us suppose that someone is an alcoholic.

He drinks alcoholic beverages to excess, and would like to stop. In order to do so, it would be very helpful if he knew why he was drinking excessively. The first set of questions that he asks his subconscious should lead him to the particular episode or episodes that caused him to seek an escape from reality into the fantasy world of alcohol. He would ask his subconscious if the cause of the alcoholism is to be found within the past five years. The subconscious will answer "yes" or "no." If the answer is "no," he would go back another five years until he localizes the trouble.

In that fashion, it can be localized to a single year, a single month or a single day. Then progress can be made to a localization of the nature of the episode, to whom it relates, etc.

When you become aware of the emotional conflicts, the precipitating causes underlying any present abnormal behavior, you will have taken a giant step toward correcting the problem. A fault known is indeed half cured.

In order to question your subconscious thoroughly, I am including in this chapter a **Conflict Check Chart.** By means of this list we will review the major causes of conflict. Be very honest in checking. While checking, pretend that you are the diagnostician, and look at yourself as if you were another person—the patient.

Now, begin your diagnosis.

Your Emotional Conflict Check Chart

INFANCY and CHILDHOOD   Yes **No**
  1. Did you receive excessive affection, with every whim gratified?
  2. Was your initiative discouraged?
  3. Were you strictly regimented?
  4. Did you have strict religious training?
  5. Did you experience a strong sense of sin and guilt?
  6. Were your parents demanding and possessive?
  7. Did they discuss illness and other problems in your presence?

8. Did they constantly argue?
9. Did you have constant conflict over which parent should be obeyed?
10. Were other children set on a pedestal as examples for you?
11. Were you over-disciplined, with no choice of conduct offered to you?
12. Were you disciplined by fear of physical punishment?
13. Were you disciplined by fear of committing a sin?
14. Were you taught that sex is sinful?
15. When you asked questions about sex, were you told nothing, very little, or misinformed?
16. Did your parents stay together for your sake?
17. Were you an only child? If so:
    a. were you coddled?
    b. had no competition?
    c. never learned to be self-reliant?
    d. never learned to share with others?
    e. remained attached to mother or father to an unusual degree?
18. Did you envy a second child?
    a. were you made to feel less important when the other child arrived?
    b. was the competition too difficult?
19. Were you an unwanted child?

ADOLESCENCE

1. Were your parents overly critical?
2. Did they pose as paragons of virtue?
3. Did you think of your parents as paragons of virtue and then were you disillusioned?
4. Were you denied freedom of choice, opinion, and action?
5. Were you over-disciplined?
6. Did either of your parents use pretended or actual illness to hold you close to home?
7. Was your home atmosphere unpleasant?
    a. constant bickering?
    b. pessimistic parents?
    c. lack of economic security?
    d. marital incompatibility of parents?
    e. unsatisfactory neighborhood and other environment?

8. Were you ridiculed during the awkward stage of adolescence?
9. Were you made to feel self-conscious or inferior?
10. Was your religious instruction rigid?
11. Did you receive sex instruction:
    a. from obscene literature?
    b. no sex instruction?
    c. street corner sex instruction?
12. Did you have unsatisfactory sexual experience:
    a. with your own sex?
    b. with the opposite sex?
13. Was false modesty with regard to sex shown by:
    a. your parents?
    b. teachers?
    c. religious leaders?
    d. companions?

ADULT LIFE

1. Marital problems:
   a. was your marriage an escape from an unsatisfactory home environment?
   b. did you marry for money?
   c. did you marry because of puppy love?
   d. was your love entirely physical?
   e. do you have nothing in common with your mate:
      1. intellectually?
      2. emotionally?
      3. spiritually?
   f. did your family force the marriage?
2. Are you bored with your mate?
3. Do you constantly seek escape from home?
   a. lodges.
   b. other social activities.
   c. out with the boys.
   d. bars and grills.
   e. nightclubs, and so forth.
4. Are your sex needs unsatisfied?
5. Are you unable to satisfy sex needs for your partner (or vice versa)?
6. Do your temperaments differ?
   a. you are optimistic and your partner is a pessimist.
   b. you like the company of others and he prefers to be alone.
   c. you need affection and he is indifferent.

7. Is your mental level higher or lower than his?
8. Are your religious beliefs different from his?
9. If you have a child, is there a question as to what the religious training should be?
10. Are your ideas on training your child in all respects different from those of your partner?
11. Do you have no children and don't want any although your partner does (or the reverse)?
12. Don't you feel a need for your mate?
13. Does your mate feel no need for you?
14. Have you no common interests either in his business or elsewhere?
15. Don't you enjoy sharing your experiences and activities?
16. Are your in-laws troublesome?
17. Are there financial difficulties?
18. Did sudden wealth lead to a change in attitude?
19. Do you enjoy the sex act?
20. Does your partner enjoy the sex act?
21. Do you fear pregnancy?
22. Do you fear venereal disease?
23. Do you fear that your partner is or has been promiscuous?
24. Do you feel that your partner is dissatisfied with you sexually?
25. Are you dissatisfied with your partner sexually?
26. Is intercourse always associated with argument or nagging?
27. Do you feel that the sexual demands of your partner are perversions?
28. Do you have a physical defect that bothers you:
    a. large ears?
    b. large nose?
    c. receding chin?
    d. pendulous breasts?
    e. others?
29. Have you been rejected in love?
30. Has the death of mother or father plunged you into despair and depression?
31. Have you lost money?
32. Have you lost your job?
33. Did you fail to receive the advance you expected?
34. Are your children not developing as you feel they should?
35. Do you have more troubles than anyone?

36. List here any recent acute source of worry.
37. Is your mate losing interest in you and is your illness an opportunity to keep him at home?
38. If someone else is more attractive to your mate, do you use illness to hold his attention?
39. Does your illness prevent your child from leaving home and is that just what you want?
40. Does your illness make it hard on some member of your family and you'd like to revenge yourself on that person?
41. Do you find it hard to get a job and your illness offers an easy explanation?
42. Do you like to have someone else support you?

Now that you have filled in the check list go back over it and see if you have been entirely honest. If you feel that there should be any changes made, make them.

I have presented this chart before in medical literature. I present it again because it will help you as a general guide toward training in contacting your subconscious. There are many questions in the conflict **Check Chart,** all of which can be answered by "yes" or "no." Many of these questions you would not think of asking yourself. However, they are all very important, and you should go through them all with the pendulum technique.

Your subconscious will not lie to you about yourself. And since time began, "Know thyself" has been the advice of the ages. Through direct communication with the subconscious, this is possible.

To Sum It Up . . .

In this chapter you have learned how important it is to be in touch with your subconscious. And you have learned how to contact the subconscious. When talking to your subconscious mind, you should:

1. Always give general commands.
2. Always make **positive** statements.

3. Never say **IF**.

4. You (may) use gentle, permissive command.

Your subconscious mind will obey you **completely** and **unquestioningly**.

Furthermore, with the help of the pendulum technique, you can discover how you **really** feel about things.

And finally, I have given you a **Conflict Check Chart** to help you spot problem areas in your life, both in your past and right now. You are on your way to a more complete understanding of yourself—your actions and your desires—with UNITROL.

chapter 5

Controlling Your Future Health With The Projection Method

In the previous chapter you learned how to reach and question your subconscious mind by the use of pendulum method. In this chapter I shall teach you how literally to hold a conversation with your subconscious mind. Again, you may ask direct questions and expect to receive direct answers, information of which you may not have been consciously aware.

This technique may be put into effect while either sitting or lying down. I prefer that you lie down comfortably with your arms at your side. Place yourself in a state of UNITROL Relaxation by your key word phrases. Relax completely, quieting both mind and body.

Now visualize a television screen directly in front of you. I would prefer that you choose the television screen of your own television set—it is more familiar to you and has stronger emotional content. Visualize the room in which the television set is located. See the walls, the furnishings, the colors in the room—and now focus your vision on the television set. See the set clearly. Now look at the screen. Let everything else fade from view and see only the screen.

Dial "S" for Subconscious

Now turn on your set. You are going to tune in a new channel—a channel of your subconscious mind. The channel is marked "S" (for subconscious) on your television control knob.

Soon the picture will clear and you will see yourself on the television screen. You may now ask your subconscious any question you wish relating to your problem. For example, if you are overweight, ask yourself to go back to a time when you were slim, and have your subconscious channel show you a picture of yourself as you were.

If you wish to find out why you have become overweight, ask your subconscious mind to show you the beginnings of this problem. It will do so. You may see your childhood, with your mother or father urging you to eat and eat. You may see a bad example of overeating set by your parents, brothers or sisters. You may see the times in which you felt inferior for one reason or another, insecure or unloved, and sought solace in food. You will begin to realize, as you see the past once again, that you have been using food as a tranquilizer to help you escape your problems. You will see that you have been hiding from the reality of life behind your fortress of fat. In a similar fashion, you may visualize, on your subconscious level, the sore spots in your earlier life that resulted in present problems—alcoholism, excessive smoking, promiscuity, lack of sexual vigor, impotence, etc. You may visualize the beginnings of your emotional problems that led to symptoms like migraine, allergy, colitis, or any other psychosomatic illness. Please remember that everything that ever happened during your lifetime is recorded in full detail in your subconscious mind. Every sight, sound, touch, odor, every sensation relating to every experience of your lifetime is recorded on your subconscious recording device. Now, through the magic of UNITROL projection you can replay this record and once again relive the past—on command.

This is a good opportunity to use the **Conflict Check Chart** in conjunction with the subconscious projection method for complete answers to your questions. Your subconscious projection channel will show you the answers in every detail. As you develop the technique fully, you will see very clear, precise pictures of your past. You can look back into your early childhood and even into your infancy, if you wish.

Have you had a dream that you would like interpreted? Place yourself in a state of UNITROL relaxation. Allow yourself to go into a very deep state of relaxation. Now turn on UNITROL projection. Ask your subconscious mind the meaning of your dream. You will see the drama played in full detail, giving you the exact meaning of your dream.

In the dream, your subconscious mind provided symbolic material, concealing and twisting the true dream content. Your subconscious mind will now untwist and reveal the true meaning of the dream events. You will be amazed at the significance of your dream. It will be very helpful to you in solving your current problems.

How to Create and Control Your Future Through the Projection Method

Would you like to be able to alter the future? You can do so. Project the image on your subconscious channel that you would like to see one year, two years, five years or ten years in the future. Would you like to be slim, alert, vital, young, successful? See yourself that way in your subconscious future. See yourself on the subconscious future channel "S." Keep this image before you as often as you can. See it often, see it for as long as you possibly can each day.

An excellent time to visualize a projection of the future is at night just before going to sleep and in the morning when you wake. Do this often, and your subconscious mind will set in motion the necessary mental and physical mechanisms to make this image a reality. You will become slimmer, happier, healthier, younger and more successful—if you see yourself that way —and think the proper thoughts and say the proper words to your subconscious.

Let me introduce a word of caution with regard to projections into the future. This statement is not intended to indicate that you can actually foretell the future with this technique. You cannot do so. However, you **can** mold the future. You can guide your own footsteps, hew your own path into the future. You can use this technique for good purposes, visualizing yourself in happy circumstances, healthier circumstances, with a healthier body, a stronger, more mature mind. Use the subconscious UNITROL Projection technique in this fashion to shape the future to fit your desires.

The Secret Language of the Body

Now, let us go back to the past on our channel "S," and let us ask more questions of your subconscious mind. Did you ever hear of organ language? This is the language that the various organs of the body speak when they are upset by emotional disturbances. Did you ever stop to think of the meaning of the word "heartache"? You might ask your subconscious mind, if you have the pain in your chest known as angina pectoris— "**Who** gives me a heartache?"

Or, you might ask, "**What** gives me a heartache?" Your subconscious mind will show you the answers to these questions. Once you know the answers, your heartache may decrease in intensity or disappear.

Again, a word of caution. This does not mean that organic changes are reversed by knowing the source of the trouble. They may be much improved, and coronary spasm may disappear completely once you have insight into the emotional problems that caused such spasm. On the other hand, you must continue under the guidance and care of your family physician while you are using these techniques.

Have you ever thought of the statement, "You give me a pain in the neck?" A pain in the neck may be very uncomfortable indeed; but if it is due to a particular person or a particular situation, drugs will provide only symptomatic or temporary relief. When your subconscious projection channel shows you who or what gives you the "pain in the neck" your pain will begin to disappear. Indeed, it may disappear instantly. The muscle spasm associated with such pain is relaxed when the source is discovered and made known to your conscious mind.

You Ask the Questions

If you have diarrhea or constipation, it may be because you have had a "bellyful" of someone or something. Let your subconscious mind tell you who or what has given you "a bellyful." It may help you or your physician to overcome serious bowel disturbances. Would you like to know why you are a failure? Would you like to know what or who makes you unhappy? Your life is in many respects unique—indeed, in all respects. Although it has certain general features in common with ever other life, its specific content is unique, individual, the only one that ever did or will exist.

In that sense, you must learn to phrase your own questions. You must direct these questions to the potential trouble spots as they relate to your anxieties, your emotional aberrations, your behavior problems, your illnesses. You will discover curious and unsuspected relationships between your present problems and your recent or distant, consciously forgotten past.

Remember that your subconscious forgets nothing. You now know how to speak with your subconscious. Your subconscious mind is now upon very friendly and open terms with you. When you are in a state of UNITROL relaxation, in UNITROL projection, you are in intimate contact with your subconscious mind. Ask any question you wish. Your subconscious mind will answer, in full detail, with all sensations relating to the previous episodes.

The repressed memories in your subconscious will now be released. The emotional dynamite that had previously exploded without your knowledge, producing symptoms at the conscious level, will now be detonated harmlessly by UNI-TROL projection. Let me give you a simple medical example from my own practice.

A Simple Case Made Complex
—by the Wrong Belief

One of my patients had serious diarrhea and was convinced that he was going to die of cancer of the bowel. Examination with a lighted tube (a sigmoidoscope), and with X-ray, showed no evidence of any organic disease in the intestinal tract. I was convinced that the problem was basically emotional. The emotional disturbance had produced overactivity of the large bowel, with a resultant diarrhea.

The use of the **Conflict Check Chart** and the projection technique revealed that this man's aunt had died of cancer of the large bowel. She had had diarrhea. His only contact with this aunt had been while he was a ten-year-old child. His conscious mind had forgotten that he had lived with this aunt for a period of one month, during which time her cancer had been diagnosed, the diarrhea was active, and the aunt had died.

From that point on, his subconscious mind had equated diarrhea with cancer and death. To his subconscious mind **diarrhea** literally meant **cancer.** It literally meant death. The forgotten memory—the repressed dynamite of that memory in his subconscious mind—was acting to perpetuate his diarrhea. The diarrhea might have been started by some food that had upset his intestinal tract. It was then potentiated and perpetuated by the subconscious mind, which takes everything very literally. To the subconscious mind of the ten-year-old boy—which still existed within the forty-two-year-old man who was my patient—diarrhea meant cancer and death. Acting on this premise, impulses continued to go from the subconscious mind to the large bowel, causing overactivity of the bowel and diarrhea. All this was occurring without the knowledge of the conscious mind.

In time organic tissue changes might have taken place. In time this patient might even have gone further downhill in a very serious fashion. It is even conceivable that he might have developed excessive mucous secretion (known medically as mucous colitis), and perhaps even ulcerative colitis.

Ulcerative colitis is sometimes complicated by the development of cancer. Thus, the subconscious mind might ultimately have literally translated the experience of the ten-year-old child into actual cancer and death.

When his subconscious projection mechanism made him aware of the childhood experience that he had unconsciously carried into his adult life, the insight resulted in an immediate cessation of his diarrhea. Now that he knew the source of his symptoms, he obviously no longer needed to behave at his present age as if he were still ten years old.

This was a memory that he could now file and forget at the ten-year level. It no longer acted subconsciously, his subconscious mind now having been made aware of the illogical and unnecessary unconscious level activity. In effect this is like detonating a buried land mine that might otherwise have exploded and destroyed the unsuspecting traveler. We each have many such buried land mines in our subconscious mind. We can detonate them safely, without harm to ourselves, by the use of the UNITROL projection method.

When we do so, the symptoms they might otherwise be producing, or have produced in the past, by exploding without our awareness, will be stopped or prevented.

Obviously this is an extremely valuable technique for you to learn. It may be literally lifesaving for you to learn how to converse with your subconscious mind. This technique will enable you actually to control or eliminate symptoms, get rid of emotional conflicts, make you happier, healthier, and younger. It may save your life.

Two Therapies that
Help You Project a Fuller Life

Now that you have acquired the ability to communicate with your subconscious mind, I want to introduce you to two kinds of therapy that will strengthen the projection technique and will help you to have a healthier, happier, more productive life. These are Expectation Therapy, and Enthusiasm Therapy.

How Expectation Therapy
Can Work for You

To a large extent UNITROL utilizes "Expectation Therapy." The subconscious mind tends to create in fact whatever the conscious mind feeds it as expectation. In that sense it is very much like the "electronic brain." It works on the data fed to it by the operator. It cannot provide its own information, its own data. But once the electronic brain (the subconscious mind) receives from the operator the information that it needs for consideration of the problem, it goes into immediate action, and the solution of the problem is soon forthcoming. In the case of the electronic brain the solution appears on a card or tape. In the case of the subconscious mind the solution is realized through the actions of the body. Thus, if you feed the subconscious mind misinformation, you will get the wrong solution. If you feed it the correct information, you will get the right answer to your problem.

If you feed it thoughts of ill health, the solution will be a disease. If you feed it thoughts of good health, the solution will be a healthy body, a vigorous vitality.

If you expect to be well, you will be well. If you expect to be ill, you will be ill. If you expect to be poor, you will be poor. If you expect to have enough for your needs, your subconscious mind will make that the reality. If you expect to sleep, you will have a restful night. If you expect to be awake, your subconscious mind will torment you throughout the night.

If you anticipate an asthma attack, you may be sure you will have it. If you expect a migraine headache, your subconscious will co-operate, the blood vessels in your brain will go into spasm, and you will have your expected headache. It is perhaps better to say "desire" instead of "expect." If you desire a headache, you will get it. If you desire an asthmatic attack, you will get it. If you desire to be overweight, you will stuff yourself with food. All these desires are efforts to escape the realities of life. They are the coward's way of retreating from battle.

Take the case of Fred C. as an example. Fred's father and mother were both alcoholics. Everyone in town expected Fred to grow up "to be a no-good drunk like his father" or "a lush like his mother." Fred didn't try to be anything else. At twenty-seven, after being found drunk and unconscious on Skid Row, he was admitted to a hospital where I was working. He told me, "I don't know why anyone should be surprised. They all expected me to be a drunk."

But Fred did not have to be what **other people** expected him to be. Only **he** talked to his subconscious.

And only **you** talk to yours. So choose your words with care. Expect success, happiness, good health, and whatever else you desire. Your subconscious will go to work to make your expectations reality. As you **project** and **expect** your future, so it shall be.

A Brighter Life
Through Enthusiasm Therapy

And finally, I should like to emphasize **Enthusiasm Therapy.**
The French call this **joie de vivre**—the joy of living. Do you
take pleasure in living? Do you rise in the morning with a
smile, face the day with excitement and enthusiasm and antici-
pation? Do you enjoy the blue skies and the clouds? Do you
enjoy the rain, the wind, the snow? Do you enjoy the sunshine?
Are you aware of the flowers and the trees? Do you pause and
listen—really listen—to the songs of the birds? Do you hear
the rain, feel it, enjoy its caress? Do you really feel every experience deep in your heart and soul? Do you really use your
eyes the way God intended, your ears really to hear, your taste
really to enjoy each morsel of food, your touch really to become aware of and caress everything within reach?

Become aware of everything that goes on within you and
around you. Become aware to the point where you are keenly
excited by the very simple things of life. You are constantly
surrounded by miracles. You, yourself, are a miracle.

Begin your day with a smile, and keep the smile on your
face all day long. When you do that you will be amazed to see
the answering smiles on the faces of everyone else. People who
don't know you will return your smile. And you will notice an
amazing thing within yourself. When you smile, you feel better, no matter what trouble you may have.

And do you laugh enough? Laughter is excellent medicine.
It will do you more good than tranquilizers, barbiturates, sleeping pills. It will do you more good than vitamin injections. You
really can laugh your troubles away. Enthusiasm Therapy demands **joie de vivre,** smiling and laughter.

Remember the old Eastern proverb: "A man should rise
with the dawn and wash his heart with laughter." If you do
this, you already have an advantage over the person who finds

life humdrum and dull. You will find that Enthusiasm Therapy can make you attract others like some wonderful lodestar, for no one wants to seek sadness and misery, but we all love the person who makes us feel happy when we see him.

Forget yourself, you are really an inconsequential assortment of atoms on a larger group of atoms we know as the earth, a speck of dust among many millions of other specks of dust spinning about in this vast universe. The troubles that you consider to be so important, the problems over which you fret away and destroy your very life, are really of little consequence when you see them in proper perspective. Take the God-like view of yourself, the earth and the universe. You will realize then how truly insignificant you and your troubles are. Seeing that, burst into a hearty laugh at yourself. When you have learned to laugh at yourself, you will be well on the way to recovery from emotional and physical illness. While **projecting** the future you desire, you will **expect** that which is good and positive, and so you will free yourself to plunge into the future with the joy and confidence of reasoned enthusiasm.

To Sum It Up . . .

Your subconscious mind **never forgets anything.** In a state of UNITROL relaxation, employing the UNITROL projection technique, you can converse with this part of your mind in great detail. Remember, you are the actor on the stage. You can:

1. See the past, overcoming old fears and traumas.
2. Fix your present, seeing more clearly what you are here and now.
3. Visualize the future you desire.

And you can start making that desire real through UNITROL.

Use the **right** words, **positive** words when you address your subconscious, and REPEAT, REPEAT, REPEAT! Your subconscious is yours to command!

You have also learned about Expectation Therapy and Enthusiasm Therapy. Begin now to use these techniques to achieve a happier, healthier, more successful life—the life you have dreamed of!

chapter 6

Earlier in this book, I told you how to achieve control of your voluntary muscles. Now that you have

How To Master Involuntary Muscle Control

mastered that phase of UNITROL, plus achieving the ability to communicate with your subconscious, you are ready to go on to a most important UNITROL technique—involuntary muscle control.

This technique will require more concentration from you. You must WILL yourself to master this chapter, for in terms of your future, it offers you the ability to slow the aging process, to rejuvenate yourself. Youth and vitality can be yours—through mastery of your involuntary muscles. So you see this is a most important chapter.

How the Subconscious Controls the Involuntary Muscle System

The involuntary muscles are the smooth muscles of the body, muscles that control the blood vessels of the body, the movements of the bowel, the movements of urine down the tubes from kidneys to bladder, etc. They are internal muscles, we cannot see their action, and we cannot ordinarily control their functioning.

However, the subconscious mind **does** control the action of these involuntary muscles, the glands, the heart, the lungs, the intestinal tract, and every other organ of the body. The subconscious mind is obviously a fantastic mechanism.

And this remarkable mechanism is under our direct control if we use UNITROL techniques. UNITROL makes it possible to contact and command the subconscious mind. Bear in mind that once the command is given, you need only sit back and relax. The subconscious mind will do the rest.

Remember that nothing is impossible to your subconscious mind. It controls your internal functions 24 hours a day, every second of every minute, ever minute of every hour, every hour of every day and has been doing so since before you were born. All you are doing now is establishing a proper rapport between yourself and your subconscious mind. You are doing this through the scientific techniques of UNITROL. You are doing it by uniting in one all-powerful method the immense powers of body, mind and spirit. You will command your subconscious mind.

These commands will be most effective if they are given repeatedly. Each of us varies in his capacity to command the subconscious mind. We have had so many negative commands, so many confusing orders implanted in the subconscious mind since childhood that we have to get rid of much of this chaotic material before we can attain pure control. When you were a child, for example, you may have been told that you were a bad boy (or girl), that you were sloppy, careless, inefficient, that you would never succeed, etc. Many negative, confusing thoughts of failure or inadequacy have been implanted in every child's subconscious mind. Such negative thoughts, in effect, **commands,** have been given to our subconscious minds every day of our lives since we were born. We have been scolded, reprimanded, ill-advised, badgered, poorly informed, and handled at cross purposes by our well-meaning parents, our teachers, our guardians, our friends and enemies. We have received conflicting information from radio and television. We have received disturbing impulses and have seen murder, rape, wars, pillage, and all the human and animal base emotions on television, in the motion pictures, theaters, on the stage, and perhaps even in our own lives.

Is it any wonder that we come to an adult state of life, confused, anxious, reacting badly, with many character traits that we would like to change? Is it any wonder that the subconscious mind, in which all these impressions have been carefully registered, is sometimes confused as to what is expected of it. It must be treated gently, retrained in proper channels by repetition, by time, by the UNITROL techniques. Once your subconscious is so retrained, it will perform wonderful miracles for you, even including control of the hitherto uncontrolled internal functions of your body.

You will be able to slow the rate of your heart at will. You will be able to lower your blood pressure at will. You will be able to produce a bowel movement if you are constipated, and slow the motion of the bowel if you have diarrhea. Obviously, control over your heart beat and your blood pressure can help retard aging. Nothing ages us more or wears the body down quicker than tension. Tension shoots the blood pressure up, speeds up the heart. But through UNITROL you can combat tension and fight this unnecessary aging process. Indeed, once you realize the powers of the subconscious mind, as you do now, you need only use the UNITROL techniques to achieve these results right now.

She Was "Talked"
Into Heart "Disease"

But before we go on to instruction in how to control these most important muscles, let me tell you about a particularly striking example of someone whose involuntary muscles nearly killed her.

Carol M. was, as a child, nervous and delicate. Since she was an only child, Carol was watched over constantly by her too protective mother. If she ran and played, was **normally** active, she was reprimanded by her mother and always reminded that she must "take good care" of herself.

Carol grew up believing that something was wrong with her physically. As she grew older, she worried more and more about her health. When she began to worry, she noticed her heart beat rapidly. This frightened her into believing that she had "heart trouble."

I met Carol, not as a patient, but as a friend of her family. I knew from the beginning that she was a tense, worried person, but it was only after she was married that this became really serious.

In the normal course of marriage, Carol became pregnant. I had not seen her for several months, until she dropped in one evening while I was visiting her parents.

I took one look at her, and as a doctor, I was frightened. She was deathly pale, gaunt, her hands trembled, and in her eyes was a look of panic, I **had** to speak to her alone—and I did.

After a short time spent denying anything was wrong, she broke down and began to weep. Twisting her handkerchief between her fingers, she told me how she **knew** having this baby would kill her! She had so convinced herself that her heart was weak that she was sure she would not come out of delivery alive.

After having her checked to be sure her heart was sound, I instructed Carol in UNITROL. I showed her how, with the help of her mother, she had "talked herself into illness" and how she could "talk" herself out of it.

When the time came, she had a labor with no problems and she gave birth to a fine son. But she **might have died** during delivery had she not learned of UNITROL relaxation. Her subconscious mind **could have killed** her.

So you see how important it is to retrain the subconscious mind so that we can healthily control the involuntary muscles.

Smooth Muscle Control—
What It Is and What It Does

Some of you, because of confusing early memories and experiences, may have some difficulty in achieving this ultimate depth of control. However, it will be possible for all of you with practice—and with complete faith in and knowledge of your deep indwelling powers. Remember that these are the powers of God in your subconscious mind. They are **your** powers, for it is God's will that you act for Him, through Him, with Him, in using your subconscious mind.

Now I will tell you how to achieve this wonderful state of deep relaxation.

Lie down on your bed or couch.

Command yourself: UNITROL—RELAX!

If you have been practicing your UNITROL relaxation technique, this will immediately place you in the first phase of UNITROL relaxation.

Now, repeat a single word to yourself—over and over again, allowing no other word or thought to come into your mind, picturing yourself at the same time going deeper and deeper into a state of UNITROL relaxation. The word you will repeat over and over is DEEPER, DEEPER, DEEPER, DEEPER, DEEPER. . . . . .

Keep repeating this word with monotonous regularity. Repeat it aloud. Indeed, it is a good technique to speak the commands of UNITROL aloud whenever possible. You will be practicing this and all the UNITROL techniques while alone, in all probability. It is best to do so while alone, unobserved, in the privacy of your own room. Speak aloud so that the subconscious mind will also receive the impact not only of the idea, but of the auditory effect. The subconscious mind will also receive impressions from motions of the lips, tongue and vocal cords. This combination of impressions increases the effect on the subconscious.

Take a Lesson from the Bear

Perhaps you would like to imagine yourself in the same circumstances that the bear chooses when he hibernates. You are in a dark, warm, sheltered cave. You are lying on a supremely soft bed of pine needles. You are going into a deeper and deeper state of UNITROL relaxation. Your muscles are completely stilled, your brain is stilled. You are entering a deep state of hibernation sleep.

If you can, maintain the visual image in your mind, without any words at all. If you prefer to use a single word to increase the deepening state of relaxation, keep repeating: DEEPER, DEEPER, DEEPER, DEEPER, DEEPER, DEEPER. . . . . .

Now you will be completely relaxed, more relaxed than you have ever been. Everything is effortless. There is no pain, no struggle, no tension. You need only make suggestions to your subconscious mind to direct and control your body. You are in the deepest stage of UNITROL relaxation—hibernation sleep.

Remember that it is most important for you to have a deeply charged desire to reach this state. You may wish to achieve it for the experience alone, for the control that it will give you over your inner body functions, to improve spastic heart arteries and relieve heart pain, to rid yourself of spastic intestinal muscles, excessive secretion of acid and peptic ulcer or any one of a thousand other psychosomatic illnesses that can be controlled best by the deepest state of relaxation.

In this state, all cares, worries, tensions, and even pains leave you. Your body is operating on a very reduced level, and so you can now begin to feed new thoughts, new attitudes, into your body-mind unit. This is a form of Adaptation Therapy, which is used by your body automatically in times of stress.

How Adaptation Therapy
Revitalizes You

Adaptation Therapy is a protective device to be used in times of stress, just as the human body and mind adapt temporarily to serious physical injury by going into a state of adaptation. Body metabolism is lowered to its minimum level, so that reduced demands are made upon the heart and lungs and brain. Shock is very much like the "playing dead" behavior of certain animals. By playing dead, by reducing their metabolism to the very lowest level, they have utilized a natural mechanism to deceive the external threat of danger or death. Similarly, our body plays dead. This is a protective mechanism, and when the acute trauma is over, and the body forces have rallied sufficiently to restore normal function, the body will cease playing dead. The shock state will subside, and heart rate and volume, blood pressure, respiratory capacity, and all other body functions will gradually return to normal.

In that sense, the deepest state of UNITROL relaxation is a form of adaptation, a reduction of body metabolism to its minimum level so that there will be little demand upon your vital organs. This provides an opportunity for strategic withdrawal and regrouping of your vital forces so that they may come back to the attack upon your anxieties and problems, refreshed, renewed, revitalized.

To Sum It Up . . .

Mastery of the involuntary muscles—smooth muscle control —is achieved through commands given to the subconscious mind. You can help prolong your life, be more youthful, and much healthier once you master the deepest form of UNITROL relaxation.

1. Begin with UNITROL—RELAX
2. Then go DEEPER, DEEPER, DEEPER . . .
3. Remember the bear, and keep practicing until you achieve UNITROL relaxation hibernation.

Now that you have learned how to control your total muscular system, we will go on to important and vital changes to be made in your mind—through UNITROL.

chapter 7

How Guided Association Therapy Helps You Discover The Secret Behind Your Sickness

Soon I will show you that forgetting can not only be good for you, but also, that it is often very necessary if you are to fully live your life in health and freedom from stress. However, before any forgetting is undertaken, you must first learn to make memories harmless and painless, because you do not want to put anything out of your consciousness that may be dangerous. You must prevent thoughts from festering in the subconscious and then springing upon you in the form of psychosomatic ailments.

In this chapter I will show you how to use the Guided Association Technique to make painful memories harmless, so that you can ultimately forget them without fear or difficulty.

How to Reach the Silent Level

Your first step towards this goal of health involves learning more about the subconscious mind. To learn about the subconscious mind it is well to consider the way that conventional psychotherapy works.

Psychoanalysis and most other psychotherapies, such as counselling, take place almost entirely on a verbal level. In this type of treatment the patient **talks** about his childhood,

91

his present life, and the possibilities of the future. Both the
patient and the physician are merely manipulating symbols—
words, words, words.

Occasionally, during conventional analysis, the patient actually relives a situation of emotional conflict, and he may show
rage, burst into tears, or display other deep emotion. At such
points, the patient has touched his **silent level.** This is the level
of tears, grief, rage, all types of emotion. These emotions are
recorded and often repressed at this level. They are forms of
buried emotional dynamite. They are silent only because they
are repressed, hidden, painful memories.

Obviously, the silent level is far from silent once it is brought
to expression. Once we contact this level and release the emotional content, we relive the rage, tears, grief or other emotions
of the repressed experiences. It is my belief that adequate
treatment can only be achieved (or is mainly achieved) by
contacting the silent level.

Rid Yourself of Dangerous Emotions

Now we come to the important clinical application. Words
describing an emotionally disturbing situation in which you
may originally have cried desperately are not that situation.
No matter how many words you use, no matter how vivid your
description, the words are merely words and nothing more.
They do not represent the life experience except at a verbal
level. At the silent level the emotional conflict can only be ex-
pressed by tears, actual living grief and bodily expression,
and this can only be achieved by reliving the original situation
with full affect.

Let us assume that the loss of a mother, the trauma and im-
plications of which were never fully understood, was a major
factor in the cause of the present problem or psychosomatic
illness.

And let us assume, further, that this loss left a deep emo-

tional scar at the silent level. And now let us finally assume
that this emotional scar has been a major factor in the cause
of your present psychosomatic disturbance. Picture yourself—
perhaps as a child of six (or at whatever age this occurred)—
crying desperately in grief and terror, knowing that your
mother is dead. Now consider the passage of years, and see
yourself as an adult at the present time. If you are merely talking about your mother's death, as recalled in memory, you
will just be using words, with little emotional impact. There
is very little relief of the emotional pressure of the great loss
you have suffered. Obviously, the verbal level may have only
slight emotional content inasmuch as the passage of time, and
the conventions of a society, have made it necessary for you to
repress your deepest emotions, your true feelings.

How Guided Association Therapy Works

But in guided association therapy you actually relive the
death situation with full emotional content. You are actually
six years old. You actually cry bitterly in terror and grief,
pretty much as you did at the time of your great loss. These
tears, sobs, the **feeling** of terror and grief, are expressions of
your silent level repressed emotions of the past. The benefits of
this therapy will result from the silent level release of emotions. The more fully you relive the experiences in this fashion,
the more beneficial the treatment.

As a matter of fact, repeated reliving of the emotional disturbances is essential. You must go over and over it, reliving
it as fully as possible each time, with all the emotions of the
original experience, until you can, finally, relive it without being too deeply disturbed. Ultimately, if this therapy is correctly performed, you will actually be bored or you will burst
into relieved laughter. **Repeated reliving of the emotional
stress is the essential element.** Guided association therapy in-
sists upon such reliving until almost complete emotional dis-

charge is achieved. Only then can you relax. Only then will the repressed emotions be fully released, the dynamite exploded harmlessly.

Psychiatry speaks a great deal about insight. If we define insight as an awareness of basic factors responsible for stress, we may say that when you have achieved this you have achieved insight. But more important than that, you will have fully released the emotional content of those disturbing episodes. In my opinion such release of silent level repressed emotions is more important than insight resulting from verbalization, intellectual level insight.

Why Guided Association
Is "Different"

This is my major point of departure from conventional analytical therapy. In analysis you may achieve an understanding of your problems on an intellectual level. You talk about them, and it seems that you are aware of the problems and have "understanding." However, such insight is merely the result of verbalization, and emotional elements remain repressed at the silent level. In Guided Association Therapy, on the other hand, the emotional charge at the level at which emotional disturbances act is contacted and released. It seems to me that until this silent level is reached and its emotional content discharged, symptoms will persist despite extensive verbalization, despite hours, months and years on the analyst's couch.

UNITROL techniques, by enabling you to contact your silent level through direct communication with your subconscious mind, and to relive the emotional sore spots of your life, effectively discharge the repressed emotions on the silent level. Symptoms disappear as if by magic. Actual body changes take place, leading to healing of diseased tissues, prolongation of life, and perhaps literal rejuvenation in many areas.

I do not mean to say that talking about your problems is not

valuable. It is very valuable indeed. Though in my opinion
silent level therapy is basic and most important, verbalization
is also very important. Many of our emotional disturbances
may not have had an original content of tears, grief, rage, etc.
They may have been times of emotional confusion and conflict.
The problem then is not so much the release of emotion as it
is one of better understanding.

UNITROL techniques, by providing a date for the disturbing event, making you aware of the fact that you have merely
abstracted one or more disturbing elements and therefore have
an incomplete picture, make it possible for you better to understand and dispose of such emotional conflicts, anxieties or
confusions.

Further, once you have trained yourself in these UNITROL
techniques you will have a means of guidance in the future.
When future conflicts arise you will be able to classify them
effectively, date them, index them, file them, understand the
fact that the picture is incomplete no matter how much you
think you know about it, and thus be less disturbed by the conflicts. You will be able to handle any emotional experience
more comfortably, and without producing symptoms or actual
tissue changes.

How Your Silent Level
Can Help or Hurt You

If you stop and think about it you will realize that life is
lived chiefly on the silent level, within your skin envelope.
Each of us lives within his own skin envelope, and it is practically impossible to communicate unless we have had similar
experiences. No matter what we say about our experiences, our
feelings, the words are not the experiences or the feelings. The
actuality is recorded on the silent level of our nervous systems,
the silent level of our body tissues.

When you prick your finger, you experience pain within

your skin envelope. This is a silent level experience. No matter what you may tell me about the pain, no matter what words you use in your descriptions, you cannot transmit an impression of that pain to me or to any other human being if we have not similarly pricked our fingers with a pin. All your experiences are obviously unique, individual and on the silent level.

All the important life processes (and, for that matter, all the unimportant ones, also) are on the silent level. Words may be skillfully used to describe the beating of the heart, the motion of the intestinal tract, the contraction and relaxation of muscles and any other body functions, but these are, after all, merely words. The **actual** body function occurs on the silent level. This is the level of the recording of the function, the recording of the actual living experience within the body tissues. Words may be involved in the experience, but the recording is a great deal more than merely words. Obviously, words cannot ever adequately describe any situation, any experience on the silent level, to another person who has not had a similar sensation or experience.

Remember that every sensation, every experience of your lifetime, has been recorded in some unknown fashion on the tissues of your body. The strength and depth of this recording varies with the intensity of feeling in the original experience, the quality and character of the disturbances, the attention you gave to that situation, the capacity of your sense organs and nerve pathways, and many other factors.

Your Personal Recording

Think of these sensations as recorded very similarly to the recording on a phonograph record or an electronic tape. Such recordings, faintly or deeply grooved, will persist throughout your lifetime. Actually, with the passage of time there is often a lessening of intensity. However, more often the intensity remains the same as at the time of the original recording, but is merely repressed.

The most important recordings, from the point of view of symptoms and tissue changes, are those with strong emotional content. Any life situation containing strong, unresolved emotional content results in a potentially symptom-producing recording at the silent level. The death of a loved one is such a situation.

Curiously enough, with the passage of time all subsequent experiences involving loss, tears, the sight of a dead person, link with this original experience to form an interconnected chain. That is why, many years later, any one of these factors may pass down this chain of recordings to reach the silent level content of the original experience.

Obviously, such chains of experiences are very intricately interlinked throughout a lifetime of experience. There may be connections on the visual level, on a sound level, a smell level, indeed, on all levels of sensation. And these linkages exist from one day to the next, one month to the next, one year to the next, throughout your lifetime. And this is another reason why free association—verbalization of ordinary analysis—may fail. It takes many years of talking to travel through the intricately interlinked experiences of a lifetime. There is much rambling about in many directions, often entirely away from the "sore spots" of the silent level. Much valuable time is lost in such verbal explorations. UNITROL Guided Association Therapy reaches these sore spots rapidly, releases the emotional "pus," and frees the body from the related symptoms and tissue changes.

Let the Silent Level Work for You

Inasmuch as all important life functions are on the silent level, new meaning is found in affirmations for living such as "Let yourself go," or "Relax and enjoy life," etc. Obviously, the full enjoyment of life can only be on the silent level of experience. Just talking about life is not enough. You have literally to live it within yourself on the silent level, the level of actual life experience.

As you go through the seconds, minutes, hours, days, months and years of your all-too-short life, stop and live as often as you can in the **now** silent level. This will increase your enjoyment. Even flavors of foods will be sharpened and accentuated. Become aware of what you eat, and do not merely use the mouth for rapid transit to the stomach. Enjoy every mouthful, searching for new flavors, new sensations and pleasures.

Don't look without seeing. Become aware of the color of the sky, the brilliance of the sunshine, the beauty of the clouds. See the magic of the grass, the trees, the flowers about you.

All at once your wife, children, your friends will become real experiences for you. You will be seeing them as they are, in full color, experiencing them as you perhaps never did before, more truly and fully at the silent level.

Train yourself to use your sense organs fully. Experience all sensations and emotions **now**, not in terms of partial attention, past memories or future plans.

Learn the Three Steps
for Self-Understanding

Let me summarize for you now the principles of silent level and guided association therapy as you have learned them in UNITROL:

1. **The word is not the thing.** Although we react to words as if they were things, you now will realize that actual life experiences are not on a verbal level. They are on the silent level of recorded emotions and sensations.

2. Although I want you to live more on an emotional level,

you must learn to control this also. I do not want you to identify yourself on the emotional level with unfortunate and disturbing experiences of the past as recorded at your silent level.

For example, let us suppose that your mother had diarrhea. Let us suppose further that the diagnosis was cancer of the rectum, and that she subsequently died. On the subconscious level of identification you may now link diarrhea with cancer and death. If you are not aware of such linkage at the silent level, should you later develop diarrhea you will instantly identify yourself with your mother, and you will automatically think of cancer and death. Obviously, serious symptoms and serious disability may result.

The UNITROL techniques of Guided Association Therapy, communication with your subconscious, and reliving of disturbing experiences of the past, will enable you to avoid such identification and associated symptoms.

3. You have now learned that **silent level** experiences are not merely words. On the silent level, within your skin envelope, many processes have taken place that make up your lifetime experiences, and these include basic emotions, feelings, etc. Words may be part of the experiences, but they are only a small part.

Obviously, we are all subject to such emotional disturbances and their associated symptoms. This does not indicate mental disease, but is very common in everyday life. We are all exposed to emotional tensions and anxiety-producing situations practically every day. We all suffer to a lesser or greater degree from symptoms based on such stress situations. In that respect you have plenty of company. Every patient in the physician's office, every person you know—whether he knows it or not—has emotionally based symptoms, causing functional or organic changes in his own body. It is not a question of neurosis, psychosis or mental disease. This is normal for everyone. That is why UNITROL therapy should be understood and practiced by everyone. We all need it, whether or not we know it.

How Old Are Your Problems?

Your purpose is to uncover emotional disturbances that you have repressed, perhaps for a very long time. When you learn to face the disturbing reality of your past, you will find in many cases that you have long outgrown such problems. Just facing them will be enough to make you realize that the problem you had as a child should not disturb you as an adult. You are now an older and wiser person, and there is no need for you to react today as if you were still a child. Actually, when we allow the emotional reactions of our past to act upon us in the present—at a subconscious level—we are literally carrying our childhood reactions to our adult life. We are then merely children in adult bodies.

The simple recognition of this fact will lead you to uncover and better evaluate the childish emotional reactions of your past, and will help you to face your present problems as an adult. You may be surprised to find that simple recognition of such childish reactions of the past to emotional problems that were very important to the child (but no longer important to the adult you), may be enough to rid you of all symptoms relating to the disturbing past.

You must realize that your present symptoms may be the result of a failure of adjustment during childhood, or an unhappy home environment. You may have had very little love during that period, perhaps the result of premature death of a parent, divorce, or an unsatifactory relationship between your parents.

Learn to Examine
Your Life Situation

Consider the level of your ambition in its possible relationship to your symptoms. Perhaps your ambition has been frustrated or channeled into other directions. Perhaps you are not doing the type of work you enjoy. Perhaps you are not progressing satisfactorily either in position or economically.

Your marriage relationship may be unsatisfactory either with your wife or with your wife's family. Or there may be a problem between your family and your wife's family. Any one of these factors may be responsible for an acute emotional, symptom-producing situation.

If you are unmarried, there may be difficulty in your adjustment to sex needs. Your symptoms may be a substitution for a proper sexual outlet.

If you are married, it may be that sex does not give all that you had expected from it.

Or, psychosomatic symptoms may be the result of an undesired pregnancy, or a fear of pregnancy. Again, a basic—perhaps unconscious—fear of pregnancy may keep you sterile. An understanding of this problem, plus the relaxation techniques of UNITROL therapy, may help you to overcome such sterility.

If you are in the menopausal age group, this physiological factor may be related to emotional disturbances. The frustrations of a lifetime may break through a barrier that had been sufficiently secure until the superimposition of menopausal changes.

These and many other factors will become evident to you when you review your emotional **Conflict Check Chart**. Thus you will obtain leads for the next phase of guided association and therapy.

Now, get a pen and notebook. You have some very important
writing to do.

The Truth About Your Problems

An excellent idea is to start with your earliest memory, and
then write down all the major disturbing situations of your life,
month by month and year by year. This technique of an out-
lined autobiography, together with your emotional **Conflict
Check Chart,** will lead you to the key disturbances.

However, inasmuch as you may voluntarily or unconsciously
conceal many disturbing episodes, it is important that you
utilize UNITROL techniques to reach your subconscious for
repressed or suppressed answers.

I have already mentioned the death of a loved one, because
this is frequently a source of disturbing symptoms in later life.
The death of loved ones should always be extensively and fully
relived during Guided Association Therapy.

Make a list of the people you hate, and the episodes during
which your hatred developed.

Make a list of the people you love, and then go through this
list and **describe the characteristics in these people that you
hate.** It may seem odd to you that you can love and hate anyone at the same time. However, it is perfectly normal.

You cannot love anyone all the time. No one is perfect,
including yourself. Therefore, you may find emotional disturbances deeply keyed to the person you love the most.

The very fact that the **Conflict Check Chart** can be used by
everyone should indicate to you that although your case is
unusual and unique, each of us fits into a general pattern.
Literally thousands of patients have been relieved by these
techniques, and you will probably achieve the same result.

The Vital Steps
of Guided Association Therapy

1. As you now see, the technique of UNITROL Guided Association Therapy is simple. In order to reach your sources of emotional disturbance you merely go back in your memory to the time these unpleasant things occurred. For example, if you lost your mother, it is necessary that you go back in your memory to the time you were notified of her death, and relive your reaction of that time.

2. However, you do not wish to recall it merely as memory. You must relive the experience in your imagination as if it were actually occurring right now. When you speak of that incident, or any other, speak in present tense. For example, you might say, "I go to the telephone and my father speaks to me. He says, 'Son, Mother just died.'"

3. Then you must go on to tell exactly how you reacted, as if you were reliving that period of your life at this very moment. And you must not merely talk about the experience—you must **feel** it. In other words, I want you to relive the entire experience, crying if you feel like it, noticing and describing and **feeling** once again what you saw, heard, felt, touched, smelled. You must re-experience that time as completely as possible.

See everything exactly as it happened. Notice the clothing everybody wears, including yourself, the colors of the walls and the furnishings in the rooms. See everything that goes on in great detail, and in color if possible.

Hear every word spoken. Hear the intonation, sense the emotional content of the words. If you spoke at that time, speak again now, with great emotion if your words called forth such emotion originally.

Smell every smell of the original episode, taste every taste, feel every feeling, relive every emotion.

4. When you have gone through the entire episode, switch

off the channel. Now think about that phase. Does it still disturb you in the present as much as it did in the past. If it does, then I want you to relive it all over again. And I want you to keep reliving it, again and again, with more and more emotion each time—until finally the episode either bores you or leaves you laughing. When this occurs you will be ready to **file and forget** the entire matter. It will never trouble you again.

5. Now go on to the next episode on your list and do exactly the same thing. Do this with every disturbing event of your past on your list, until you attain boredom or laughter. When you are bored by reliving the experience, or when you can see the episode and yourself in proper perspective and realize how really unimportant the whole thing was (No matter how serious it might have been at the time), you are cured of that event. It will not produce emotional disturbances, it will not keep you awake, it will not produce symptoms in the present.

The Importance of Full Feeling

I cannot stress enough the fact that you must relive each experience with full emotional content. The release of tears is an important factor in the release of the emotional charge of most painful incidents. The initial recounting of the experience may be relatively free from emotional content. If it is, you must go back over the incident once again, and attempt to bring out more and more vivid related details. The episode must be very vivid and real to you.

You must really involve yourself emotionally—you must really **feel** it in the same way you did the first time you lived through it. The most important phase of this type of treatment is the emotional release resulting from repeated reliving of the disturbing episodes.

Again, a word of caution is required. To avoid intensifying the emotional problem of a previous life situation, giving it deeper significance with each repetition, it is important that there be full emotional discharge by tears, rage, grief, or whatever emotional content there may have been in that episode. Unless there is such discharge, it is entirely possible the repetition will result only in giving a deeper significance to the problem rather than a lessened one. However, the safeguard of dating, filing and forgetting will help avoid this result. UNITROL offers several such safeguards to help make your Guided Association Therapy practically foolproof. As I have said, the technique has worked for thousands of patients and it will work well for you.

Let Key Words Guide
Your Thoughts and Solve Problems

After you have gone through the key situations (those that have been obvious sources of emotional disturbance in the past, as discovered by your emotional **Conflict Check Chart** and autobiography studies), you should use general key word stimulation. General key words are those that I have found, by experience, to be effective in restimulating problem situations for the average patient. They are part of the normal pattern of life for most of us.

Repetition of each of the words (one at a time), in the following list, in the relaxed, quiet privacy of your guided association room, may lead you down the memory linkage of your own experiences to a disturbing situation in the past. If it does, you must relieve that situation with full emotional content.

1. Your pet name
2. The words your father and mother used when they were angry with you
3. Your father's name
4. Your mother's name
5. Your mate's name
6. Your lover's name
7. God
8. Hell
9. Death
10. Life
11. Soul
12. Body

13. Poor	32. Insane
14. Sick	33. Pain
15. Bad	34. Headache
16. Evil	35. Stomach
17. Devil	36. Misery
18. Hate	37. Hit
19. Shame	38. Fist
20. Ashamed	39. Fight
21. Jealous	40. Afraid
22. Greedy	41. Dark
23. Stupid	42. Night
24. Angel	43. Black
25. Saint	44. Blind
26. Stop	45. Dumb
27. Tell	46. Idiot
28. Secret	47. Darling
29. Crazy	48. Sweet
30. Devilish	49. Dear
31. Mad	50. Little

The various UNITROL techniques for consulting your subconscious mind, as described in other chapters, will help you to
reach the key emotional situations. Relive each, in turn, as
fully as possible, until you have discharged all related emotions. Remember at all times that the goal is the discharge of
repressed emotion. The search is for **grief** in your past.

But do not overlook the fact that more recent emotional
conflicts may be triggering your psychosomatic illness. You
must not overlook recent marital experiences, quarrels, business failures, loss of friends, money, relatives, etc.

When you combine this technique with the file and forget
which you will learn in the next chapter, you will have an
excellent chance of relieving your symptoms and reversing
organic tissue changes.

How to Find the Secret
Behind Your Sickness

During the course of tracing back the linkages of your current symptoms, in searching for the earliest points of origin,

you will often find a childhood illness at the roots. During that illness the care and sympathy of your mother, father or nurse may have deeply influenced the present perpetuation of your illness. By reliving such early episodes, by reactivating and re-experiencing this early care and sympathy, you will rid yourself of present symptoms. You will no longer need to escape from your present failure into a period of time in which you were successfully cared for and looked after. Do not seek refuge in the past. Face your current failures realistically. Accept them if there is nothing you can do about them, and go on from there to improve your life situation as best you can. The crutch of illness, based upon sympathy and affection you received with childhood illness, is not the answer for you as an adult. When you become aware of the fact that you are using such a crutch (if you are), present symptoms related to such past illness will spontaneously disappear.

Let us once again emphasize the fact that the earliest related illness or emotional disturbance containing sympathy, sheltering, tenderness, solicitude, close attention and care must always be discovered. Until this is reached, current symptoms relating to that episode may be reactivated. Discharging the emotional content of more recent episodes in the chain of events will relieve the symptoms, but may not result in permanent disappearance. However, once you understand the significance of these events, and properly date the earlier disturbances, even in a general sense, improvement will be rapid. The combination of dating and guided association release of emotional content is the best.

Sit down now and prepare a careful list of the earliest illnesses you suffered, the earliest accidents, emotional disturbances, and especially those illnesses and accidents containing symptoms of your present psychosomatic illness. This history will help you trace back your interlinked chain of emotional disturbances well into the past.

You will be interested to observe that physical improvement will begin as soon as you discharge the emotional content of

even one such episode. There will be a spontaneous increase
in sense of well-being as these painful emotional episodes are
fully relived, relieved and discharged. Results will be best, of
course, when the entire life chain of disturbance is fully
drained of emotional content.

How to Stop Being "Hypnotized" by the Past

It is important for you to recognize and understand that
your every action is initiated by, bound up with, or directed by
words or symbols. The key words, phrases or symbols of each
of your past acute emotional episodes or conflicts, and of each
illness, act throughout a lifetime. As I have repeatedly said,
these are the key words, phrases and symbols that you must
seek in checking the **Conflict Control Chart,** writing your autobiography, and preparing the various lists of your problems.

These key words, phrases and symbols, registered at an unconscious level during episodes of previous emotional disturbance or illness, literally have the effect of a command, as in a
posthypnotic situation. Perhaps you have seen a stage hypno-
tist work. When his subject is in a state of hypnosis he tells
him that when he comes out of hypnosis he will perform a certain act at a specific time—usually something strange and
consequently funny. This is called a posthypnotic suggestion,
and takes effect at a later date, minutes, hours or days after the
time of the original hypnosis. Similarly, commands registered
at your unconscious levels during these disturbing emotional
incidents of your early life act at later dates right up to the
present in your own life. In a very real sense they become posthypnotic commands, effective throughout your life.

And again, I want to emphasize that not every chain of
emotionally disturbing episodes or illnesses dates back to
childhood. The initial disturbance may be in your very recent

adult life, and yet may result in marital quarrels, business loss, or other difficulties.

The death of a loved one, a spouse, child or parent, may occur late in life and initiate symptoms. It must also be recognized that contradictory posthypnotic-life command phrases may be found in emotionally disturbing situations, resulting in considerable confusion. You will not know, at the unconscious level, which command to obey.

In other words, you will really begin to understand why you behave as you do, and why you have your present symptoms. Once you understand the reasons, once you realize that you no longer **need** to have symptoms resulting from emotional disturbances that happened in the past (often many years ago), it is obvious that the symptoms will disappear. Thus, you literally have the cure within yourself.

To Sum It Up . . .

In this chapter you have examined how important it is to contact the silent level within you, and you have learned how to do this.

Using Guided Association Therapy you have:

1. Written your autobiography.
2. Listed those you love and hate.
3. Listed problem areas in your life.
4. **Relived** painful experiences until they no longer hurt.
5. Optimistically projected into the future, seeing yourself as healthier and healthier, happier and happier, and more and more successful.

With UNITROL you are on your way to overcoming all negative influences in your life. You are on your way to being the person **you** want to be.

chapter 8

How would you like to be born anew? Wouldn't it be wonderful, not only to be

How To Make Selective Amnesia Work For You

born anew, but be able to start life over again with all the mature knowledge and experience that you now possess as an added bonus? This can be done. Selective amnesia makes this possible.

What is amnesia? Amnesia is loss of memory. A person is said to have amnesia when he has forgotten his past. This is considered an abnormal state of mind, a "disease" process.

Obviously, if a person suddenly finds himself in Chicago without any knowledge of who he is, what he is, or where he came from—and if that person normally lives in New York, and has left behind him a wife and three children—there is something very wrong. For some reason his need to escape the reality of his life has become so great that the protective mechanism of amnesia developed. When he could no longer stand his wife, his life, his past, he simply forgot them completely. He did not do this purposely. His brain did this for him, unconsciously, to prevent a more serious mental, emotional or physical breakdown.

Amnesia may also develop as a result of a head injury. In such cases, however, there is always the question: Is this person actually seeking escape, and is the accident merely a convenient "excuse" for the amnesia?

111

However, we are not concerned with spontaneous or traumatic amnesia of this type. We are concerned with the **principle** of forgetting, the importance of forgetting, and the development of conscious selective amnesia as a therapy. Obviously, this is very different from the general amnesia of mental or physical illness or injury.

In selective amnesia we **choose** to forget our unpleasant past experiences. And when we forget the troubles of the past—our failures, our difficulties, our inadequacies—we automatically release tremendous energies for constructive purposes. Energies that had formerly been held in check by anxieties and problems of the distant past, memories of our failures, are automatically channeled into useful, constructive areas. It is literally like being born again.

Not All Memories Are Good

We attach great value to training our memory. It is, of course, important to be able to remember. It is important to remember the names of people we meet, to remember places, to remember our social and business contacts, to remember whatever knowledge is required in the practice of our business or profession. It is important to remember and be aware of our obligations.

However, although the knowledge and lessons learned from the sadness and despair of unpleasant and unfortunate past experiences are of value, constantly dwelling upon the actual experiences is not only of no value, but positively harmful. It is this activity of our brain that does so much harm to us—acting through the subconscious—both mentally and physically.

As you have now learned, many of our illnesses are due to negative thinking resulting from such unpleasant memories in our subconscious. In this chapter, therefore, we are concerned not with training for a better memory, but rather with training for **selective forgetting.** When you have developed this capacity for forgetting, when you have learned how to selectively forget the misfortunes of your past, you will automatically become a happier and healthier person. Amnesia training can be of even greater importance than memory training.

However, before proceeding with a description of selective amnesia techniques, I should like to tell you something about the new attitudes that must be developed for selective amnesia.

The Power of the Present

One of the major changes in attitude required to help you develop selective amnesia is to become more appreciative of the present. You must learn to count your blessings and forget your troubles.

Your major blessing is one you take for granted. **You are alive!** It is the major, perhaps the only, purpose of life: to stay alive. And so, with very little effort on your part, the greatest blessing God has to offer, life itself, is already yours. You are better off than Napoleon. You are better off than any conqueror that ever lived, any financier, better off than the most handsome movie star, the wealthiest potentate that ever trod the earth, better off than anybody, no matter what his accomplishments—if that person is no longer living. You have something he can never again possess. You have life itself. **You are alive!**

When you fully appreciate the fact that you are alive, you begin to realize that it is still possible to achieve your fondest dreams, to reach even your most ambitious goals.

I once had a patient, a well-to-do business executive, who was so worried over the possibility of business failure, so preoccupied with death and the possibility of disease that instead of living as one of the happiest of men, as indeed his position indicated he should be, he was one of the living dead. So concerned was he with negative thoughts, with gloom-

ridden attitudes that, though in perfect health, he did not
enjoy his life until too late. Not until overtaken by a fatal illness did he realize that life has value, that life is to be lived
to the fullest, every day, and that each moment must be ap-
preciated for its own sake.

So don't be like the pessimists of the world, no matter what
your position—especially since you now know that your
thoughts can make you sick or well. Take a moment, take every
moment, and savor your existence. In short, Live! Live all you
can!

Don't forget this when you start counting your blessings.
Life is the greatest blessing anyone can have.

And now, for the second great blessing you possess: You are
sufficiently healthy to remain alive. No matter what illness you
may have had, and no matter what illness you may now suffer
from, you obviously have sufficient vital energy to be alive
at this very moment, to be reading this book. To be healthy
enough to remain alive is the next great blessing that you
obviously possess.

Would you sell your life for a hundred million dollars?
Would you sell whatever residual health you have, if it cost you
your life, for two hundred million dollars? I doubt that you
would answer either of these questions in the affirmative. These
blessings are beyond price.

If you think about the money you don't have, think also of
the diseases that have passed you by. You probably don't have
a thousand and one diseases I could name, any one of which
would incapacitate you tremendously and reduce your chances
of living.

Learn to Count Your Blessings

And if you don't think you are blessed with reasonably good
health, no matter what is wrong with you, go spend the day
in the wards of one of our large general hospitals. While you

are there, study the operating room schedules. Do you still think you have no blessings to count?

Do you have two legs and two arms? Can you move all your fingers and toes, and will your joints and muscles respond when you call upon them? If they do, count yourself among the most fortunate of mortals. Go see the quadriplegics, the basket cases in Veterans' Hospitals, if you don't count this among your blessings.

Do you have the capacity to eat and digest your food? If you don't think that is a great blessing, study the number of cases on the operative schedule in the hospital where the stomach is going to be operated upon for ulcer or cancer. Ask to see the patients in the gastrointestinal section who have tubes through their nose or mouth into their stomachs, and are being tube-fed. How about the state of your digestion as a very great blessing?

Did you ever get a speck of dust in your eye and think that it must be at least the size of Mount Everest from the way it feels? Your vision blurred, your eye became red and inflamed and you couldn't see. What a blessing it was to have that speck of dust removed, to have your eye return to normal, and to be able to see. And yet you probably never thought of it that way. You have taken vision for granted, hearing for granted, taste for granted, your digestion for granted, the motion of your muscles in your arms and legs for granted, and life itself for granted.

These are all great blessings, and you should not take any of them for granted. You are here on this earth only temporarily, and you occupy your body only as a temporary tenant. If it is in reasonably good condition, be grateful for the housing God gave you. If it is in a state of disrepair, do whatever your doctor advises to put it in good condition, and use the techniques described in these lessons to assist your doctor in restoring the blessing of good health.

When your troubles seem to overwhelm you, stop, take stock

of your blessings, and say to yourself, "How wonderful! I'm alive!" Let that affirmation jerk you back on your heels, away from the yawning abyss of despondency and despair. How wonderful! You're alive! You can take it from there by adding your other blessings, by **forgetting** the past, by living right **now** to the fullest.

Stop thinking of what you lack, and concentrate on what you **have.** Stop crying over spilled milk. It is just as pointless to cry over the life that has been lived as it is to cry over milk that has been spilled. Neither one will do any good.

If you think **you** have made mistakes, and if it would not bore you, I would tell you some of mine. They are whoppers. Who hasn't made mistakes? Who hasn't committed crimes against himself and against society? Who hasn't had failures? Who hasn't lost battles? Who hasn't many regrets? The man who has no regrets or failures in his past, no skeletons in his closet, hasn't been born and hasn't lived.

It is important to develop a new attitude toward the unfortunate events of your past, to accept the fact that life is made up of experiences, some good and some bad. The more experiences you have had, bad or good, the more truly you have lived. Never regret a single one of them. The important thing is to be alive, and to be alive is to have both bad and good experiences every day of your life. So, don't cry over spilled milk; be happy that you had the milk to spill. You still have the "bottle." Refill it.

Learn to Live with Life

The next important attitude change in our training for selective amnesia is to learn to accept the things you cannot change. Have you lost an arm? Have you lost a leg? These are losses that are permanent. You must learn to live with them. I have seen a dancer dance beautifully on a peg leg. I have seen wonderful paintings created by an artist who had to hold the brush in his teeth because he had no arms. The beauty of the thoughts and writings of Helen Keller, who can neither see nor hear, is known throughout the world.

In his later years Beethoven wrote magnificent music that he would never hear, for he had become deaf. Schopenhauer was right when he included in his philosophy, "A good supply of resignation is of the first importance in providing for the journey of life." Stop fighting the inevitable; don't exhaust yourself refighting battles that are long over, and you will be amazed at the amount of energy that you release for constructive purposes. My mother used to say to me, "You must bend or you will break." That will always be true.

Remember the prayer of Dr. Reinhold Niebuhr:

> God grant me the serenity
> to accept the things I cannot change;
> the courage to change the things I can;
> and the wisdom to know the difference.

Carry a Full Schedule Every Day

Another idea you must develop in order to give up moping about the past, and to cultivate your capacity for selective amnesia, is to keep busy in the present. Make active plans for the future and spend all your time putting them into effect. Busy your mind and body with constructive thoughts and activities, and there will be no room for destructive memories, anxieties and thoughts. You must give your life purpose and meaning—by constructive thinking and creative activity.

You must become so busy that you will have no time to relive the past, no time for worry. Become fully absorbed in work and hobbies and in general living. UNITROL techniques teach you how to place positive, constructive, life-giving thoughts and attitudes in your mind. These attitudes and thoughts will crowd out destructive memories and deadly worries.

Medicine offers occupational therapy to patients recovering

from illness. We are talking about occupational therapy right now, as part of everyday living. Keep yourself occupied at all times, busy with your work, active in your UNITROL training in optimism, and you will have no time to worry about illnesses and failures of the past. You will be well on your way toward the cultivation of selective amnesia.

Alfred Lord Tennyson was right about himself, and perhaps about you, when he said: "I must lose myself in action, lest I wither in despair." Lose yourself in action and you will have no time for despair.

And now that you know about the necessary new attitudes, put them into effect, and you will have fertile ground in which to plant UNITROL seeds for the techniques of selective amnesia. Place yourself in a state of complete relaxation and repeat aloud—right now: "Every day in every way, I am getting better and better, happier and happier, healthier and healthier, younger and younger." This is your optimistic blueprint for present and future, a blueprint that the Divine Architect in your subconscious mind will use to build a happier, healthier and brighter future for you. Notice that you make no mention whatsoever of the past. You do not introduce any negative thoughts or words. You speak only of the present and future, and you speak only in optimistic terms—"better and better, healthier and healthier, happier and happier, younger and younger." That's the way it is, and that's the way it will be from now on.

Learn to Use Smile Words

No matter how bad things are, they could be worse. You are still alive, and the future lies ahead of you. Smile and the world will indeed smile with you. More important than that, your subconscious will smile with you, and the tremendous power of the subconscious will smile upon you and bring you good health, peace of mind and happiness.

Use smile words as much as you can. Use words of good cheer and optimism at all times. No matter how bad things may be, or no matter how bad they have been, put a flower in your lapel, a smile on your face, and walk forth with enthusiasm and vigor to challenge life. The world will accept you for what you appear to be—and even more important than that, your subconscious mind will accept these symbols of optimism and success and make them a reality.

Now that you know the attitudes necessary for reshaping your new life, we can go back and discard the old.

Discard Painful Memories with the File-and-Forget Method

You have learned your lessons from painful mistakes in the past. But remember, as a famous philosopher said, "Difficulties are things that show what men are."

However, now it is time to cast aside the memories of difficult times, to free yourself so that you can move forward.

First place yourself in a state of UNITROL relaxation. Now visualize a filing cabinet in your mind. The drawer is labeled File and Forget. See this clearly in your mind's eye when you turn on the subconscious channel of your projection mechanism.

Now visualize a packet of blank index cards. On each of these cards you are going to list a happening in your past. You know about "dating," and you will put a date on the top of each card to represent the date on which that particular event occurred.

Start with the first failure, disappointment, frustration that you can remember. Your earliest unhappy memory is what you are looking for. Ask your subconscious mind to picture it for you. In what year did it occur?

Make a note of the event in as few words as you can on a File-and-Forget card, and put the date on the top of the card.

See yourself writing this on the card. See it clearly. Now pull out the File-and-Forget drawer and insert the card.

Repeat this procedure for the next failure, frustration or emotionally disturbing memory of your early past. Keep doing this until you have come right up to the present moment. Keep doing this until you have placed all of these disturbing memories in your **File-and-Forget** cabinet.

Of course, when you come to the very painful, very disturbing events, you must remember to render them harmless by using Guided Association therapy. Do not allow anything in your File-and-Forget drawer that will cause you trouble in the future. Remember, **first** Guided Association, and **then** File and Forget.

Stop Living In the Past

Look upon these events as a record of someone else's past, a record from which you can profit. The person to whom these things happened no longer exists. You are not the person you were twenty years ago, nineteen years ago, eighteen years ago, ten years ago, five years ago, one year ago, or **even the person you were yesterday.** Everything changes from second to second; nothing remains the same. "You cannot step in the same stream twice." This is an ancient saying, and very true. The stream changes constantly.

You change constantly. How stupid, therefore, to react to memories of ten years ago as if you were still that age. You are no longer that person, you are no longer that age. To react today as if you were five years old, ten years old, twenty years old, or any other than your present age is immature, childish and illogical.

And yet, every time we react to the unfortunate memories of the past as if we were actually still living in the past, we are doing this very childish and immature thing. At our present age we act as if we were that uninformed and unhappy person of the past.

The overweight woman who stuffs herself today, at thirty or fifty, the way her mother stuffed her when she was ten years old, and reacts today as if she were a child of ten listening to her mother say, "You must eat if want to live," is being very immature and unwise. She is acting at thirty or forty as if she were still ten years old.

File and forget such activities of your childhood.

I know a man who suffered from hay fever for many years. As a child of seven he had been told that he was sensitive to roses, and that was the cause of his suffering. When I first saw him he was forty-two years of age and suffered miserably every time roses grew, or whenever he came into a room with roses.

One day he came into my office for consultation, and there was a beautiful bouquet of roses on my desk. He immediately began to sneeze violently, his nose became congested, his eyes reddened and the tears began to fall. He was in misery almost instantly.

I said to him, "You don't have to react today, at your age, as if you were still a child of seven. This is a memory that you should file and forget. Stop reacting to it at your present age."

"How can you say that?" he protested. "You know that I'm sensitive to roses. I always have been."

I then moved the bouquet of roses closer to him and said, "These are plastic imitations." His rose fever was cured that day. He has never again reacted in the present as if he were living in the past.

Do the same thing with your unpleasant memories of the past. File and forget them, and stop reacting to them today as if you were still the child or immature person of your past. That past is gone. You must file and forget it.

We have all made mistakes in the past. Some have been more

serious than others. We have all committed crimes at one time
or another. Some of us have been caught and have paid the
price. Others have escaped the consequences. However, we
continue to pay the price to ourselves. Our crimes of the past,
our failures and frustrations, our unfortunate and immature
behavior still haunt us and rob us of sleep and health.

Once you have learned the technique of filing and forgetting,
you will be on your way to selective amnesia. You will be born
anew.

Keep in mind that selective amnesia embodies remembering
as well as forgetting. You must begin by remembering that
you are alive in the present, and that, since you are alive, you
have a very great blessing. Once you fully realize this, and
realize that you must occupy yourself with constructive tasks
and constructive thoughts, then, and only then, are you ready
to begin the second major step in selective amnesia therapy—
the File-and-Forget technique. In this way, you fill your present, invest positively in your future, and finally, you remove
the crippling events of your past.

To Sum It Up . . .

You have learned the importance of forgetting in these six
steps of selective amnesia therapy:

1. You count your blessings.
2. You stop crying over spilt milk.
3. You accept what cannot be changed.
4. You keep busy **in the present.**
5. You use "smile" words.
6. After disarming dangerous memories through Guided
   Association, you use the File-and-Forget method.

2

USING UNITROL TO RID YOURSELF OF SICKNESS, WORRY, AND PAIN

chapter 9

How To Conquer Anxiety With UNITROL

General anxiety is the term for what people commonly call "worry"—worry over bills, worry over health, worry over position, worry over any number of things. Worry is a killer. Worry kills by causing mental disease, heart disease, and many other disturbances of the human body.

Obviously, if you want to be healthy, you must overcome your anxiety or worry.

There is no drug to treat worry. The barbiturates, bromides and other sedatives, the great variety of tranquilizers, merely mask the source of anxiety and quiet the nervous system. They are of temporary benefit, and the dosage must be repeated at regular intervals if anxiety is to be controlled.

But UNITROL can produce permanent character and attitude changes. UNITROL utilizes the natural powers that are built into your body, particularly in the subconscious mind, but also in every other cell, tissue and organ of your body. With UNITROL, you do not need drugs of any kind to help you relax. You do not need drugs to produce tranquillity or peace of mind. You attack, root out and control the basic causes of your anxiety. You learn new attitudes, and change your character structure. The new "you" does not need drugs. The new "you" will not worry any more than is absolutely necessary on a day-to-day, problem-to-problem basis. The new

125

"you" will not live in the past, nor die from the anxieties of the future.

Learn to Live
One Heartbeat at a Time

Obviously, UNITROL is exceedingly important. Before we go into specific techniques for the application of UNITROL for general or specific anxiety, let me discuss with you some of the important character and attitude changes we are seeking.

In my book, **Immortality—Pathways to Peace of Mind,*** I stress the importance of living life one day at a time. We go still further and urge that you live life one moment at a time. Indeed, you cannot live more than one heartbeat at a time. And yet, most of us live in the past, continually tormenting ourselves with our failures, our frustrations, our incompetence in past performances, and further torture ourselves with the possibilities of failure and illness in the future. When we occupy our minds with such thoughts we lose sight of the present moment. As far as we are concerned, the present moment never really exists. Remember that you can only be aware of the present moment if you concentrate your attention upon it. You must think about it. You must hear every sound right now, smell every smell, see every sight, feel everything there is to feel, taste all possible tastes. You must use your awareness and senses to the fullest if you are to enjoy this moment right now. If you don't, you will be living in the torment of the past or the fantasy of the future. You will certainly not be living right now.

There was once a famous physician, Sir William Osler, who advised his students to live each day in "day-tight compartments." The same advice was given by a much greater phy-

---

* Available from the UNITROL Teaching Institute, 147–41 Sanford Ave., Flushing, N. Y.

sician, many hundreds of years before, when Jesus Christ said, "Have no care for the morrow. Sufficient unto the day the cares thereof."

The first step to peace of mind is to accept the things you cannot change. They are finished, they are in the past. Leave them there. Your only concern is with the present and with your efforts to shape a better future.

Say to yourself, "Every day in every way I am getting better and better," and you automatically replace your anxieties about the past with the recognition and realization of improvement in the present and the future. This is an all-important phase of UNITROL anxiety therapy.

Now that you have eliminated all anxiety about the past, and have agreed to start afresh today, you must learn a new technique for approaching your day-to-day anxieties. We all have problems and will continue to have problems in the future. Life is a war made up of many separate battles. You will lose many of the battles, but as a good general you now know that it is only important to win the war. The number of battles you lose is of no consequence. Even the great Napoleon lost one-third of all his battles. Remember that every executive who makes important decisions makes at least 50 per cent wrong ones. This does not make him a bad executive. Indeed, he is a very good executive if he keeps his percentage at that level. You are a very good executive of your life if you have only made 50 per cent wrong decisions to this point.

Keep your enthusiasm for living and keep your spirit high. If you have lost money, you can earn more. But if you have lost spirit, you are indeed in danger of losing the war.

UNITROL will help you to retrain your spirit and give you a new zest for living. With UNITROL you can inculcate enthusiasm deep into your subconscious, so that it becomes a part of your very being.

Chart Your Worries Away

Problem solving should not be a hit or miss affair. You must first carefully and honestly analyze the problem. Set down all the facts related to your worrisome situation.
Ask yourself, and write down in a notebook:

What is worrying me?
Why does it worry me?
Why is it important?
What is the worst thing that can happen to me?
Will that probably happen?
What is the next worst thing?
Will that probably happen?
What can I do about this worrisome situation?
  Nothing? (If this is true, will worry help?)
  Very little?
  Several things? (If so, what are they?)

Make your plan—a positive plan based on a real analysis of your problems.

When you have done this, figure out what the future holds. What is the worst that can possibly happen? It goes something like the old joke, "If you are sick, you have nothing to worry about. Either you will get well or you will die. If you get well, you have nothing to worry about. If you die, you certainly have nothing to worry about."

The worst that can possibly happen to anyone is that he will die. If your problem does not involve death, why worry about it? Analyze the difficulty, make the best plans you can to meet the problem, and then stop worrying about it.

Your most important objective—indeed, your only fundamentally important objective in life—should be to remain alive. If you are alive all things are possible to you.

If you are married and happy with your family, your next most important objective beyond remaining alive is to remain together. A happy family unit can overcome any adversity.

Therefore, once you have analyzed all the facts of your problem, and have faced the possibilities of the future, you really have nothing to worry about.

When you have learned to co-operate with the inevitable, and have mentally said to yourself, "If I lose all my money I will still be alive and can earn more"—when you have faced the possibility of ruin, disgrace, failure, and have learned to live with it in your mind—you will be ready to meet the present challenge of your problem.

Remember that most of the things we worry about never happen. We very often spend sleepless nights torturing ourselves with the possibility of failure, loss of money, disgrace— wasted nights, because these things never happen. When they do occur it will be soon enough to deal with them. However, accept the worst as a reality, face it and determine in your mind what you will do should this become the actuality—and then forget about it. You have made your basic plan to enable you to overcome the worst that can possibly happen. Now do everything you can to prevent it from occurring.

Having faced the worst, having planned for it, rather than worried about it, you can devote all your time and energy to a strategy to prevent an unfavorable outcome to your problem. When you stop worrying, you release an immense amount of energy for constructive purposes.

Kill Worry
Before It Kills You

Worry is a destructive emotion, a deadly emotion, one the subconscous picks up and spreads throughout the body-mind. You must learn, in UNITROL, how to replace this deadly emotion with constructive thinking, optimism, inward certainty that you will work your problem out successfully.

Place yourself in a state of UNITROL relaxation. Visualize
yourself as successful, the problem favorably solved. Now
repeat to yourself three times:

*—I am content. Every day, in every way, I am coming closer and
closer to a successful solution.*

The last affirmation is particularly important and effective.
It indicates that improvement is continuous, and the solution
to the problem is developing well. It places the subconscious
in the position of certain victory, and leaves the details to
that all-powerful subconscious mind.

Another useful affirmation is: **It is the will of God that I be
successful.** Believe this completely, place this affirmation in
your subconscious mind during deep UNITROL relaxation,
and you can safely leave the rest to the natural processes of the
subconscious mind.

Remember, you can only expect the subconscious to do
everything within its power to guide and control your own
actions in a favorable direction by your attitude, your state of
mind, the positive optimistic affirmations you feed it.

Let us assume that in this particular problem situation the
worst does happen, through no fault of your own. Remember
the first step and don't cry over spilled milk. Accept the inevitable, cooperate with it, make the best of it. I will always remember Dale Carnegie's admonition: "When fate hands you
a lemon, make lemonade."

Remember that you cannot win every battle. Relax now in
the realization that you have fought the good fight, that you
have enjoyed the battle, and that although your head is bloody,
it is unbowed. Your spirit can never be broken, for it is the
spirit of God that lives within you.

Again place yourself in a state of UNITROL relaxation and
say, "From now on, every day in every way. I am getting
better and better, happier and happier, healthier and healthier,

younger and younger." With this state of mind, with this un-conquered spirit, it is literally true that nothing will be impossible unto you. The future holds many more challenges, and many opportunities to solve problems successfully. Life is yet to be lived.

Right now, drop everything, sit back or lie down, and relax completely. Allow yourself to go into a deep state of relaxation. Now let all your worries evaporate for the moment. Later on you can analyze the facts of the present problem, figure out the worst that could possibly happen, and adjust yourself to that—and then fight to overcome your problem.

But right now I want you to start fresh. Relax completely and let yourself go. Let every muscle go limp and loose and use the UNITROL relaxation key phrase of your choice. Then add the following magic words: **"It is the will of God that I succeed."**

How to Conquer
Your Specific Anxiety

Now you know many of the UNITROL techniques to help you get rid of negative attitudes and to help you handle general anxiety. Next I will show you how to handle your specific worries through UNITROL.

The Big Problem: Money

Let us first consider financial worries. The basic principle to learn is that everybody has financial worries. Can this really be true for the millionaire? Yes, I know many millionaires, and they all spend the majority of their time worrying about money. If they have one million, they are worried about earning two million. If they have two million, they are worried about earning three or four million. They are never satisfied,

and spend their waking hours scheming further big deals.
They disturb and distort their sleeping hours by similar
plans.

They also have very big worries about losing their money.
They do not make real friends, inasmuch as they feel everyone is out to take advantage of them, and is interested only in
their money. And usually this is true. They are worried about
their daughters and sons, for many reasons. One of the reasons
is related to money.

They are fearful that a fortune hunter will marry their
daughter for money, rather than for love. The man with a
great deal of money worries about his son, and whether or
not his son will carry on the business, add to the fortune or
dissipate it. He is also worried about the gold digger who seeks
to marry his son.

And so, you see, vast fortunes do not necessarily bring con-
tentment and peace of mind. They bring great responsibilities.
They are a challege that is not adequately met by most millionaires or multimillionaires.

However, as Joe E. Lewis, the famous comedian, has so
correctly said, "I have been rich and I have been poor, and
believe me—rich is better." Money is important, money does
talk. It is essential to have a sufficient amount to take care of
your needs and the needs of your family. It is not necessary to
have millions, nor is it necessary to maintain a standard of
living beyond your means. It is not necessary to keep up with
the Joneses, or to be concerned in any fashion with the activity
of the Joneses.

If you have lost all your money, even if you are bankrupt,
it is not the end of the world. As long as you are alive, the same
capacities, the same qualities of mind and body that made it
possible for you to earn the first fortune will make it possible
for you to earn another. Many men have lost more than one
fortune, and have lived and died rich. Again, it is not the loss

of the battle that counts, nor the loss of many battles, but the fighting of a good fight, the joy of living, and the outcome of the war.

If you have been thinking only failure or mediocrity, that is precisely what you will achieve. Your subconscious mind creates in fact what you have yourself created first in thought, exactly like the architect who plans a building. His ideas, his thoughts, are translated into drawings and blueprints. The drawings and blueprints in turn become the reality.

You are the architect of your own realities. Your thoughts and ideas, whatever you envision, are the blueprints which will become realities in your life. Think big, act big, and you will be big. Think small, act small, and you will be small. Any degree of success you choose will become the reality.

You should now place yourself in a state of UNITROL relaxation, or you may do it at bedtime, or just before you waken in the morning, and you will give the following affirmation to your subconscious mind: "Every day in every way, I am becoming wealthier and wealthier." I would suggest that you merely add to this your general affirmation as follows:

Every day in every way, I am becoming happier and happier, healthier and healthier, younger and younger, wealthier and wealthier.

Health "Worries" and How to Stop Them

Another major source of specific anxiety is ill health. If you are worried about your general health, yet suffer no specific illness, you probably belong in the large category of functional illness patients. The vast majority of patients who come to the average physician's office—at least 90 per cent—are functionally ill, and have no organic disease. In very simple language, the illness is due to worry. They may have symptoms relating to many parts of their body. Indeed, the more widespread the symptoms the more likely it is that the illness is of emotional origin rather than organic.

Sometimes such patients are classified as hypochondriacs. Sometimes the physician calls them neurotics. It all comes down to the same thing—they are so worried that their subconscious mind translates the worry energy into body symptoms. UNITROL relaxation is particularly helpful in controlling these disturbances.

The relaxation techniques combined with the general affirmation, "Every day, in every way, I am getting better and better, happier and happier, healthier and healthier, younger and younger," will control and overcome these psychosomatic problems. Study the preceding lessons carefully, and practice the techniques daily. You will then overcome emotionally based illness without the aid of drugs.

Specific health problems can be handled in two ways. First, the general UNITROL affirmation technique will start the subconscious mind in the right direction. Remember that the subconscious mind contains within it the immense powers of God. These powers know precisely what tissue changes are necessary in your body to correct your illness.

The specific approach to your individual disease, if localized tissue changes have already taken place in some organ, such as the heart, the lungs, the stomach or the intestinal tract will be considered in detail later. We will discuss the major diseases separately. However, the general affirmation method can be used until then. This will start natural healing processes in action right away, without delay. As I have so often said, your subconscious mind knows what your tissues require for healing better than you do. Therefore, even when we have specific illness in specific organs, it will be unnecessary to issue detailed instructions to those diseased tissues or organs. You can safely leave the details to the subconscious mind. After all, your subconscious mind has been running your body without any help from you, and in spite of your unconscious or conscious efforts to destroy it, since before you were born.

How to Ease
Domestic Tensions

Your anxiety may relate to a domestic problem. If you are having difficulty with your mate, review the **Conflict Control Chart** you prepared earlier. Perhaps you will discover something about yourself that, if changed, could alleviate your tensions.

Remember, you are not perfect. Why should you demand perfection from a partner? Just as I have urged you to accept the difficulties in life, to learn to live with what cannot be changed, so I must urge you to accept your partner as he or she is. There are some things which cannot be changed. Acceptance Therapy can help you to make your marriage a success.

But accepting imperfections is not enough. Remember the power of Enthusiasm Therapy. If you truly project the **joie de vivre** this therapy can give, no one around you can remain tense and unhappy.

Also, just as you made a worry chart for your general anxiety, make a marital problems list. Ask yourself: What is wrong? When did it begin? Why did it begin? Am I at fault? How can I change? What must I do? What can we do?

Get in touch with your subconscious for the answers. Use the Pendulum Technique combined with the Projection Technique.

No problem is too big for you if you practice all your UNITROL techniques. As you do, as your character changes, and as you become a happier, more optimistic person, you may be surprised that many of the irritations of married life drop away. You might add to your affirmation: "Every day in every way I love my wife (or husband) more and more." Your subconscious will then surprise you by putting this into effect.

You will become more solicitous, more tender, more affectionate, more loving. As you give more love, you will receive more. "As ye sow, so shall ye reap."

At all times, feed health-giving thoughts to your subconscious just as you feed health-giving foods to your stomach, at regular intervals. Upon arising, when brushing your teeth, when applying your makeup or shaving, while driving to work, while returning from work, at mealtime, at bedtime, repeat to yourself, "Every day in every way, I am getting better and better, happier and happier, healthier and healthier, younger and younger." Your subconscious will make all of this come true.

To Sum It Up . . .

Worry is a killer and so it is very important that you **stop worrying**. Learn to live one heartbeat at a time, enjoying **this present** moment.

By making a worry chart and a marital problems list, then asking yourself questions that I gave you, you can pin down the **causes** of your worry.

Finally, you can overcome these worries through UNITROL projection and UNITROL Enthusiasm Therapy. You can kill worry instead of letting it kill you. It's up to you—with UNITROL!

chapter 10

Pain is nature's warning signal. When you feel pain you know that something is wrong. It may be a serious organic condition, with tissue

How To Reduce Anguish and Pain

changes requiring urgent medical care, such as a closure of one of the arteries that carries the blood to the heart (the coronary arteries). It may be a simple muscle spasm, such as a charley horse or a muscle spasm at the base of the neck, causing a stiff neck, or spasm of the muscles around the eye, causing pain behind the eyes, or headache.

It may be a functional pain due to stress and emotion, muscle spasm being the actual pain-producing element.

It may be the pain of a stone moving from the kidney through the ureter (tube leading from kidney to bladder). It may be the pain of a gallstone attempting to pass down the tube from the gallbladder to the small intestine. It may be the pain of muscle spasm in the small intestine, or more commonly in the large bowel.

There are thousands of potential causes of pain, and you should never attempt to make a diagnosis yourself. Always seek competent medical advice when there is any persistent abnormality, particularly pain. It is indeed nature's warning signal.

Curiously enough, we do not want to prevent pain unless we know that the particular pain we are preventing has been accurately diagnosed as emotional in origin. We do not want

137

to take away our God-given signal that warns us when something is seriously wrong. We need this signal so that we will obtain proper medical attention before the disease process has progressed beyond human help.

However, until such time as medical help arrives, it is of great importance to you to be able to **control** severe pain. And it is certainly important to have the capacity to help your physician in his treatment by controlling your own pain as much as possible without drugs.

How wonderful it is to be able to snap a switch in the brain, so that no pain sensations reach the level of awareness. This can be done when you have trained yourself in UNITROL pain control.

By the practice of the technique I am about to describe you can also learn to produce numbness in any part of your body. This will be valuable to you if you are planning to have a baby. It will be valuable to you if you are planning to have dental work at any time. You will be able to relax completely in the dental chair, without fear, knowing that the area of your jaw requiring treatment will be numb, and under your complete control. Indeed, you will even be able to control bleeding to a large extent. Still further, wounds will heal faster, and there will be less tendency to infection.

The Secret of Pain Diversion

Bear in mind that you will be using a very normal mechanism in the elimination of pain. Remember the many times when you were a child, or when you saw a child fall on the concrete sidewalk and skin his knees, bruising them badly and perhaps bleeding actively. What did the child's mother do? She simply said, if she was wise, "Oh, darling, did you break the sidewalk?" By thus distracting the child's attention from the bruised and torn knee, and diverting that attention to the sidewalk, the brain ceased to receive or be aware of the pain impulses coming from the injured knee.

The Power of Positive Affirmation

Or she said, gently substituting an affirmative, pleasant thought for the pain sensation, "Let Mother kiss it, and the pain will go away." Thus, she provided emotionally charged symbols of love and healing, together with the positive affirmation that the pain will go away—and miraculously enough the pain did go away.

How different it would be if she were to become panicky, shout and scream at the child, or scold. The pain would be very much intensified and the child would also scream and suffer.

This is a very simple, everyday example of how a positive affirmation, emotionally charged, can very quickly turn off the switch and stop pain impulses from reaching the level of awareness. It also shows how you can turn off the switch yourself, as the child does, when your attention is diverted elsewhere. When the child worries about having broken the sidewalk, he disassociates his mind from the painful area, directing his full attention to the sidewalk. Again, the brain receives a substitute visual stimulus in the search for a broken sidewalk, replacing the pain impulses that would have otherwise gone to the brain.

Here we have two separate methods to control pain. (1.) directing the attention elsewhere, and (2.) substituting a positive statement that the pain will go away in place of the thought that might otherwise exist in the brain—"Oh, how that hurts!"

The gentle, understanding, calm, controlled mother transmits her own calmness and control to the child. She does this by the tone of her voice, the assurance in her actions, and the reassurance of her words. She does it by gently caressing or kissing the injured area. This is another part of the pain-removing technique that you can use. You may gently stroke

the painful area, saying to yourself, "Going, going, going,
going—gone!"

The simple repetition of this word, rapidly, firmly, gently,
calmly, has the effect of occupying your full attention, and is
very much like looking at the sidewalk for a break in the
concrete. Still further, the meaning of the word adds to its
effectiveness, and the rapid repetition makes it difficult, if not
impossible, for the brain to think pain, or "Oh, how it hurts,"
or any other negative, disturbing fear-thought.

How to Practice
Pain-Relieving Technique

When you practice these pain-relieving techniques you
should first place yourself in a state of complete relaxation.
This is important because much of the pain that we suffer
is due to muscle spasm. Most headaches, including the very
disabling migraine type, are emotionally produced, and spasm
of muscles or spasm of blood vessels is the basic pain-producing element. If you practice the UNITROL relaxation technique for voluntary and involuntary muscles, you can relieve
most of this pain.

Think how valuable it would be for you if you had angina
pectoris, or even if you knew that you were developing a
serious coronary closure. You may feel as if your chest is in
a vise. The pain may radiate from your chest to the left side
of your head or down your left arm, perhaps as far as the
finger tips. Such pain may come on with exertion or severe
anxiety, or after you have had an exceptionally heavy meal.

If you become terribly upset and afraid at such a time, the
pain will get worse. Increasing pain will increase your fear,
and this in turn will increase both spasm and pain. Nothing
could be worse.

The Magic Key
to Pain Relief

You now hold a magic key to relief of such pain without drugs. If you are sitting, try to lie down. Whether sitting or lying down, place yourself in a state of UNITROL relaxation by using the key words of your choice. As soon as the muscle spasm comes under control, much of the pain will disappear. You will then calm your mind by stating, "The pain is going, going, going, going, going—gone!" At the same time, you will symbolize the mother's gesture of love, and soothing, pain-dispelling caress, by gently massaging the area of pain with your hand. Gently squeezing the skin over the involved area will very often help in hastening disappearance of the pain by substituting another sensation for the pain.

This is an excellent way to handle acute pain until such time as your physician can be consulted. After proper diagnosis you may use the technique freely to assist your physician in controlling or preventing future painful episodes.

If an actual coronary occlusion (closure of the coronary artery by a clot) is occurring, this pain control technique may make it unnecessary for you to have large amounts of morphine or other narcotics. This will be a great advantage for you because large doses of narcotics are potentially dangerous. The less you need, the faster you will heal, and the less danger there will be of a serious drug reaction.

Another advantage is that the calm relaxation produced by UNITROL is a very important element in increasing the rate of healing. Fear can kill. UNITROL eliminates fear.

How to Overcome Pain
with UNITROL Projection Technique

Chronic pain can be handled in precisely the same way, utilizing the relaxation, "pain going, going, going—gone" affirmation and the touch of the reassuring, emotionally charged hands. In this way UNITROL projection techniques can be used to eliminate or reduce chronic pain of advanced cancer, or the pain of a kidney stone or a gallbladder stone, before the stone is passed.

After you have attained a state of deep relaxation, you may prefer to visualize a gentle hand touching the area of pain, and you will then say: "The pain is gone. It is the will of God."

If you have faith, "even as a grain of mustard seed," pain will disappear instantly. As your experience with this technique grows, and as your faith in the subconscious, and in the indwelling God power grows, your ability to relieve pain will increase rapidly.

Another excellent projection technique as you rest quietly in deep relaxation, is to visualize yourself on a screen at some future time after the pain has been controlled. See yourself at that time, happy, carefree, free from pain. As you develop a strong image of yourself in this relaxed, happy state, your mind will become completely disassociated from the pain, the pain impulses will cease to reach the level of awareness, and you will actually become the person you visualize—**yourself free from pain.**

Or you can visualize yourself at a past time, before your illness began, when you had no pain. Again, the technique is the same. You have either seen yourself in the future, cured of the illness and pain, or in the past, without the illness and pain. The subconscious acts out the positive nature of this visual image. You may use auditory impulses as well, by hearing yourself say, in your vivid imagination, "I feel wonderful. Every day in every way I am getting better and better."

Remember that it is the will of God that you be happy, healthy, normal, free from disease and pain. Give your subconscious mind and the God-given power within it the proper command, and it will eliminate pain and help you restore your body to better health.

How to Understand
the Role of Pain In Your Life

If your pain is of emotional origin, it is important to learn why you **need** the pain. It seems odd to think that you might actually **need** pain. However, any illness, including painful illness, may be an attempt to escape reality. There may be a disturbing financial problem, or there may be a distressing domestic situation. You may be unhappy at work. There may be many reasons for you to be emotionally upset, and unconsciously to seek out a painful illness to escape your responsibilities.

Pain can be **used** to keep you from activities that you do not enjoy. You do this unconsciously, of course, and you may not be aware of the fact that your illness is strictly functional —muscle spasm produced by the subconscious desire to escape your duty, work, or any unpleasant situation.

The projection technique of UNITROL may be very useful to uncover the real pain-producing motivation. Simply place yourself in a state of UNITROL relaxation, let yourself go very deeply, and then visualize the television screen. Now ask your subconscious to show you why you are suffering pain. Your subconscious will flash a picture on the screen, and you may be surprised to find that your pains, your problems, may be merely your method of escape.

Once you become aware of the real reason for your suffering, your subconscious and your conscious mind will then assure you that it is completely illogical to have such pain. You will become aware of the fact that there are better solutions to your problems.

Using the Switch Technique
to Control Pain

The switch technique is also useful for many patients. Some patients find it a very simple matter to place themselves in a state of deep relaxation, and then imagine that they are turning off a switch in the lower part of their brain, so that the pain impulses cannot reach the level of awareness. Pain ceases instantly for such patients. Try this technique and see if your subconscious likes it. If it does, it will work wonders for you.

How to Use UNITROL
In Place of Anesthetics

And now, finally, let me teach you how to make any part of your body numb at will. It is very easy to produce what is known medically as analgesia. In this condition there is awareness of touch, but not of pain. The step beyond this is anesthesia, where there is no sensation whatsoever—neither touch nor pain. This may require a little more practice for some of you, but many of you will be able to produce anesthesia instantly, and at will.

The technique is very simple. First, remember that you have done this normally many, many times when you have crossed your legs, and your foot went to sleep. What does this mean? It means that you have reduced the circulation to your foot by the pressure of crossed legs, and the foot actually became numb. When it comes out of the numb state, you feel a prickly, tingling sensation.

And have you ever been numb with cold? If you live in a cold climate, or have ever visited a cold climate, do you remember how your toes, your fingers, the tip of your nose or your ears became completely numb when exposed to the cold? This recollection may help you to attain a visual image for the production of numbness.

Or have you ever had a general anesthetic for surgery, or local anesthetic by injection? If you have, remember the experience in your imagination, and you can quickly duplicate the same sensation while in a state of deep UNITROL relaxation.

Let me show you how easy it is to use the natural powers of your subconscious to train your mind in **disassociation,** so that you will not be aware of sensations coming from the area you wish to be numb. But first, let me remind you again that such disassociation is very common normally.

Think of the husband and wife at the breakfast table, his head in the sports section of the newspaper, totally unaware of the fact that she is speaking to him. Finally, in desperation, she says, "Mother dropped dead this morning, and little Johnny had both legs amputated by a truck."

The husband absentmindedly says, "Yes, dear." He has not heard a word she said. His attention has been so thoroughly riveted on the newspaper that all auditory (sound) sensations have been short-circuited, and have not reached his level of awareness. This is normal disassociation.

How many times have you daydreamed yourself to the point that you were totally unaware of what was going on around you? You were lost in your pleasant imaginings. Again, these are examples of everyday normal disassociation, where the brain is not aware of sights, sounds or any other sensations from any part of the body or its environment. It is so interested in what is going on inside the mind, that it is totally unaware of what is occurring elsewhere in the body, or in the external environment of the body.

This is the very thing you now seek to achieve in learning how to disassociate your mind from painful stimuli coming from within your body. You are merely using a normal, every-day function of your subconscious mind, a capacity that has always been available to you.

It is this same innate power that you will now use in learning to develop numbness in any area of your body, just as if you were experiencing a local or general anesthesia.

Anesthetized by the Subconscious:
A Case History

An anesthetist once told me of a patient undergoing a Cae-sarean section (for the delivery of a baby through the ab-domen, the normal passage being too small). The anesthetist began the anesthesia by giving his patient pure oxygen to breathe through a mask so that she would have no fear when he later gradually introduced the anesthetic gases. He gave her the oxygen while waiting for the surgeon to get ready, and his own attention was directed elsewhere.

Finally, he looked up to ask the surgeon if he was ready. Horrified, he saw the surgeon holding the baby up by the heels. The surgeon had assumed the patient was getting an anes-thetic gas and had proceeded with the operation. Indeed, the operation was practically completed.

His patient was in a deep state of sleep, and had felt no pain. The patient had also assumed she was receiving anesthetic gases, and her subconscious promptly put her to sleep. No pain sensations were allowed to reach her level of awareness.

You can do the same thing for yourself, at will. If you really **need** anesthesia for pain, you will do this more easily than if you do it simply as an experiment. The patient in the above example **needed** anesthesia so that she could undergo surgery. Her subconscious knew this need and acted accordingly. The generalization of a mask over the face was enough for her subconscious to put into effect the necessary mechanism to prevent pain sensations from reaching the brain. The surgery was completed down to the last stitch with nothing but oxygen (which has absolutely no anesthetic qualities at all).

The postoperative course was completely uneventful, and mother and baby were normal in every respect.

This illustrates the tremendous power of your subconscious mind. It can produce anesthesia at will in any part of your body, or throughout the entire body.

Your Anesthetic Technique

And now we will produce anesthesia in your left hand, to show you how very easy it is. More correctly, **you** will produce anesthesia in your left hand through the normal powers of your subconscious mind. Remember that these are powers that you have always had, and have used normally hundreds of times. You are now going to use them consciously rather than unconsciously.

Place yourself in a state of deep relaxation, while sitting comfortably. Now concentrate on sensation leaving your left hand. It is rapidly becoming completely numb. You can hasten the process by saying, UNITROL—Anesthesia. This will be your key phrase to produce anesthesia in any part of the body.

Now designate the area by saying, "UNITROL—Anesthesia —Left Hand." Your subconscious will obey at once, and your left hand will become numb.

You may deepen the anesthesia, making it progressively number by saying, "Deeper, deeper, deeper, deeper, or "Numb, numb, numb, numb. . . ." When you have achieved a sufficient degree of numbness, you can test with a pin or by pinching.

You will find that you can transfer this numbness to any other part of the body by simply touching the area you wish to become numb with the numb hand and by concentrating on the key words. A transfer will take place instantly, making the other area of the body equally numb. Thus, if you need to go to a dentist, you can either make the required area of the

jaw numb directly, or you can do it indirectly by making your
left hand numb first, and then touching the area of the jaw
you wish to anesthetize.

Anesthesia:
When and Where You Need It

You will soon become very adept at this technique, and you
will find it a simple matter to produce anesthesia in any area
of the body. This will be very valuable for you in a time of
need. Indeed, when you really **need** anesthesia, as I have already said, it will be even easier to produce. The subconscious
mind will then act at once, and without question, to protect
the body by anesthetizing the area of painful injury or surgery.

Here again, the projection technique can be used during a
state of deep relaxation, if you visualize yourself while undergoing a previous anesthesia, either local or general. You now
relive the experience and become as numb as you were the
first time. Or you may imagine that an injection of anesthetic
is being given in the area you wish to make numb. You can
see and feel the injection being given, and then you will feel
the numbness developing gradually or rapidly, as you wish.

Or you can imagine an anesthesia mask being placed over
your face, the anesthetic gases developing their full effects as
you breathe deeply several times. Visualize that mask over
your face, begin to breathe deeply as you hear the anesthetist
tell you to take a deep breath, then another and another. With
each breath you go into a deeper and deeper state of sleep and
relaxation. Of course, all pain sensation disappears from all
parts of your body. You are asleep and under anesthesia.

It is good for you to know that every conceivable type of
operation has been performed under this type of anethesia
with no drugs and no actual anesthetic gases. A lung has been
removed in this fashion, an operation has been performed
inside the heart of a little girl—all without deep drug anes-

thesia. Indeed, in the days before anesthetics were known many hundreds of operations were performed while the patient was in a state of anesthesia produced by the subconscious mind.

To Sum It Up . . .

So you see, there is nothing new under the sun. UNITROL anesthesia is an old and time-honored procedure. It is a normal capacity that you have always possessed, but have only used unconsciously, without awareness. Now you will use it consciously, fully aware of this great power that you possess and control.

You will control pain by:

1. Directing your attention elsewhere.
2. Substituting the positive statement that **pain will go away** for the negative thought "It hurts."
3. Gently stroking the painful area while using key words to remove pain.
4. Using:
    UNITROL relaxation technique.
    UNITROL projection technique.
    UNITROL switch technique.

Through the miracle of UNITROL, you can conquer pain, freeing yourself for a more vital and healthier life.

chapter 11

You have now learned the techniques of UNITROL and how to apply them. As I told you ear-

Applying UNITROL To Relieve Sickness and Suffering

lier, UNITROL is effective in relieving—and often even curing—many specific diseases which are either bothersome, painful, or dangerous to life.

For your easy reference, in this chapter you will find a number of common ailments listed, along with the particular phase of UNITROL therapy that is most beneficial for each disease. Of course, when you are referred to certain sections for a specific disease—heart disease, for example—you may have to change some of the key word commands. However, by now you should be adept in the use of UNITROL, you also know the function and power of words, and you know how to choose the key command words which will work best for you.

When I refer to any phase of UNITROL in this section, I expect you to turn to that section and review it immediately. And of course, for all ailments, Expectation Therapy is extremely important. You must **expect** to feel better, and be better. Your subconscious mind will serve as a full time, private specialist working just for you, if you will only feed it the proper thoughts and beliefs, couched in the proper words, to guide it. Control of the mind-body unit can be yours, through the application of UNITROL and through faith in yourself.

151

Allergy—Its Cause and Cure

Asthma	Neurodermatitis
Eczema	Pruritus
Hay Fever	Psoriasis
Hives	Rose Fever
	Urticaria

Allergies are one of the most common and most unpleasant afflictions that man brings upon himself. They represent a special sensitivity of the human body that results in one case in difficulty in breathing, in the second case in nasal congestion and inflammation of the eyes, and in a third case in a blistering skin reaction.

UNITROL gives you a supplementary approach to control of the symptoms, rapid relief of distress, improved insight into your problem, and perhaps even ultimate cure. You must remember that in every consideration of allergy, certain questions should be raised:

What can't you stand?

Whom can't you stand?

Whom can't you stomach?

There is no doubt that the allergic individual has a delicately balanced body. He is delicately balanced emotionally. This balance is easily upset. The very expectation of attacks when the pollen season begins is sufficient to key the body-mind unit to the very edge of the attack. If we expect to be ill, we very often will be. If we know that our illness comes with the seasons, the expectation is deeply imbedded in the subconscious. Even if there is no pollen, the subconscious mind will see to it that the attack occurs in accordance with our expectations.

Thus it is obvious that the subconscious must be retrained.

The application of UNITROL techniques to your particular

allergy is twofold: (1) to relieve immediate distress, and (2) to help uncover the cause of the allergic reaction.

Many of our allergic reactions—whether in the respiratory tract, the intestinal tract, the skin, or elsewhere in the body— are childish reactions continued at our present adult level. They are reactions to emotional situations that are best brought to our conscious awareness, filed and forgotten. Here guided association is very valuable. Reliving past events until they are no longer traumatic, or until they are fully understood as **past events,** not present situations, is extremely important.

I have seen hives produced in a husband who was allergic to his wife. Whenever they had a bad quarrel, he broke out in hives. But the cause was not as simple as that. It developed, during subconscious UNITROL projection and regression into his past, that he had developed hives as a child every time his father and mother quarreled violently. His hives stopped the quarrel and brought the doctor. With himself as the center of attraction, the center of anxiety, the quarrel was temporarily forgotten. He was obviously using the same mechanism as an adult, in his own marriage. He was not allergic to his wife; he was allergic to quarreling.

Obviously, UNITROL can be very helpful in helping you to discover the truth behind your allergic attacks. You have learned how to go back into the past and make yourself aware of early emotional disturbances. You can determine the relationship between these disturbances and your attacks by asking your subconscious the necessary question while in a state of deep UNITROL relaxation. Turn on your subconscious projection set, then simply command: "Show me the cause of my attacks."

Your subconscious will help you to discover the cause of the allergy if it is emotionally based. There may be more than one cause, so be sure to work through **all** the disturbed experiences that your subconscious reveals to you.

Your physician, of course, will prescribe drugs to help alleviate the symptoms of your allergy, but there is much help to be gotten from UNITROL techniques as well.

You have learned control over involuntary body functions. You may now turn off tears at will. In hay fever, the tears are the natural protective mechanism washing irritating allergens from the eyes. Ask your subconscious if there is an emotional basis for your allergy. If so, command: "If there is no irritant in my eyes, turn off the tears."

Whatever your allergy, discover whether it is emotionally based. If so, adapt your key commands to your particular symptoms. At the same time, pursue the cause of your allergy through guided association technique until you can finally File and Forget, freeing yourself from both the cause and the allergy as well.

How to Prevent and Control Heart Disease

Heart Disease

Hypertension

Tachycardia

First, I must tell you that many cardiac invalids do not actually have heart disease. They merely **think** they do. Remember that if you think you are ill, your body will behave accordingly. Thus, the patient who **believes** he has heart disease is often as ill as the person who actually has heart damage.

It is like the man who believes he cannot move his arm. If he believes he is paralyzed, he will not move the arm; if he does not move the arm, the muscles waste away, bones and joints atrophy, and the arm becomes actually paralyzed.

The same thing applies to the heart. The heart is a muscle, a pump. Occasionally every one of us experiences palpitations—an awareness of the heartbeat. When we are very tense and anxious the heart rate may increase. This is quite normal.

However, if we live in a state of constant tension, or if we have had a close relative die from heart disease, then this normal response from the heart may send us scurrying to the doctor. If he finds a slight murmur—a thing not uncommon especially among people over forty—even if he assures us that it is nothing important, many people will be convinced that they have heart disease.

If the doctor, while taking such a patient's blood pressure, inadvertently raises his eyebrows, scratches his chin, or looks in the least worried, that patient will assume that he has high blood pressure, as well. Even though the doctor reassures him, he will go home and begin a constant round of worrying. The worrying, in turn, will place additional stress on the heart.

While worrying, he may smoke more—adding more stress to his circulatory system. He may be restless, and without realizing it, drink more coffee than usual. Then he may get a real fright, when the heart suddenly begins beating rapidly (tachycardia). He is convinced at this point that he has heart disease and must take care of himself; thus a cardiac cripple **with a healthy heart** is born.

UNITROL relaxation provides the very best possible antidote to cardiac neurosis. Deep relaxation, as you have learned, relaxes the voluntary and involuntary muscles as well. But first, one must be aware that the **fear** of heart disease is the disease, not heart disease itself. If you are afraid that you have heart disease, see a specialist. Of course, if he finds something wrong with your heart, you must follow his instructions exactly. However, even then, UNITROL can be a vital adjunct to your physician's treatment. If he finds nothing wrong with your heart, then it is time to seriously examine yourself—your fears, your anxieties, your disappointments.

Here is where UNITROL can make all the difference. Review the section on anxiety. Apply the techniques listed there. Search your past for negative suggestions and associations that may have led you to this moment when you began crippling yourself. UNITROL Projection Technique will help you to discover the source of your ailment.

Then begin a program marked by Enthusiasm Therapy, by feeding your subconscious mind the positive commands that will help it to help you to free yourself of illness.

If you have a real cardiac damage, then it will immediately be obvious to you how important UNITROL relaxation can be. I have heard dozens of people complain, "My doctor says I must relax, but he doesn't tell me **how** to do it." I have told you **how**—through UNITROL.

If you are actually experiencing a heart attack, UNITROL can help you to help yourself until the doctor comes. Lie down, place yourself in UNITROL relaxation, and say to your heart: "The pain is going, going—gone. . . ." As you know, fear and tension at such a time can only aggravate your condition. At this point, relaxation can be life saving.

Relaxation is important, of course, for anyone, even with a healthy heart. Any tension shoots up the blood pressure, throwing an extra load on the heart. This is the reason that people with damaged hearts are told to keep calm and to avoid tension-inducing situations.

Here, again, UNITROL can be helpful, for it can help you to understand yourself better, to realize why little things upset you, to rid you of past bad associations through guided association and selective amnesia, so that you will respond with new, positive reactions to difficult situations.

Most of all, however, we should concern ourselves with the prevention of heart disease. When you learn to apply the basic principles of UNITROL, when you have changed your attitudes and reduced your anxieties, you will have made a major step toward the prevention of cardiovascular disease. You will be started toward improved health and prolongation of your life.

How to Relieve General Joint
and Muscle Pains with UNITROL

Arthritic Pain
General Joint and Muscle Pain
Rheumatism

If you are suffering from swollen, painful joints, then the first thing you want is relief from pain. The reason behind the pain is only of secondary importance at the moment that burning, stabbing pain attacks.

Again, let me refer you to the chapter on pain control. If you practice your UNITROL therapy diligently, while you may not completely be freed from your pain, you can alleviate it a great deal. UNITROL relaxation is extremely important here, for it is a known fact that pain can enter the mind on different levels of consciousness.

For example, right now, if you are feeling well, stop and think of your body. Become conscious of it in great detail. Perhaps there is a small fatigue pain in your wrist simply from holding this book. Does your neck ache a little? Maybe you have been sitting with you neck slightly twisted. But you were unaware of these small pains until you brought them to the conscious level. Obviously, you do not want to concentrate on every small pain you have—indeed, quite the opposite! I simply wanted to demonstrate to you how some pain may be with us at all times, but as long as we are occupied with something that interests us, we do not notice it.

However, once we do notice a pain, if we begin to worry about it, it **will get worse.** The tension may aggravate it. But just being aware of it, thinking about it, allows it to occupy the mind, making the mind more aware—and therefore **more sensitive to the pain!** Obviously, UNITROL relaxation helps you to block the pain from your mind, thus lowering the level of awareness which in turn helps alleviate the pain.

Positive suggestions also help. For example, if you have pain in your shoulder, you can place your hand on the joint that aches, and command your subconscious mind: "This pain is going, going, going—gone." Or you may choose other command words that work for you.

Once pain is alleviated, you should investigate to see if there is an emotional basis for it. Many doctors believe that arthritis and similar joint pain results from pent-up hostility and frustration. UNITROL projection will help you to find the cause of your pain. If it is psychosomatic, then you need to pursue the reasons—frustration, hostility, or whatever—until you can understand why you feel this way. Quite often, people discover that the reason no longer is a valid one, and they are freed from pain immediately.

Of course, all UNITROL therapy should be applied in conjunction with your physician's recommendations and treatments. And remember, if there is an emotional origin for your ailment, that it probably did not develop overnight. Do not expect miracles, but work with faith and patience towards the mastery of UNITROL—the mastery of YOUR LIFE!

"Nerves" and Other Psychological Ailments Can Be Overcome

Anorexia (loss of appetite)
Anxiety
Excessive Perspiration
Fatigue
Headache
Hysteria
Insomnia
Mental Depression
Migraine
Nailbiting
Nervous Tension
Neuroses
Obesity
Psychoneurosis

Stammering
Stuttering
Tics

The variety of the ailments listed here should serve as an indication of how "talented" and imaginative the subconscious mind is when it tries to "protect" us from some painful memory or unbearable situation. You know the power of that part of yourself by now through your study of UNITROL. And you understand yourself much better by now, I am sure. Perhaps you have experienced rather obvious protective impulses from your subconscious when you began exploring the unhappiness of your past while working with guided association therapy. Perhaps you had such a bad headache, suddenly, that you just couldn't go on for a while. That headache was the protest of the subconscious against having its routine disturbed.

Your subconscious is interested, primarily, in keeping you functioning. It cannot realize that you will be happier once you face up to past fears and bad memories, and overcome them. It only knows that you need protection from psychic pain, and it gives that protection in the form of distracting (and disabling) ailments.

Or perhaps you have believed at sometimes that you were bad, or that you misbehaved, and therefore you needed to be punished. The subconscious took this belief as **instruction**—you told it to punish you, and so it does through various painful ailments.

Obviously, what is needed to overcome this type of ailment is a new look at yourself, a reevaluation of what you are and what you are worth. By now, I am sure that you are aware that this is what UNITROL is about. This whole book was written to help you to set yourself free—to help you discover the joy and peace of mind that **should** be, and **can** be, yours.

All of the various techniques of UNITROL can be employed beneficially to help you understand and overcome psychologically induced ailments. Remember, you have the ability, the power, and now, the knowledge to help yourself—with UNITROL! Believe in a positive, triumphant self, and you will triumph.

How to Combat
Genito-Urinary Tract Ailments

Frigidity
Functional Sterility
Impotence
Menopausal Problems
Menstrual Problems
Premenstrual Tension
Urinary Retention

The ailments of the genito-urinary tract are often psychosomatically induced. I am sure you can readily see how this might be possible.

For example, obviously a woman who finds the sexual act repulsive, or who fears pregnancy, might suffer from extremely painful periods. Her anxiety settles in the physical area related to the cause of her anxiety. Or she may have horrible premenstrual depression, with accompanying bad temper and discomfort for a week to ten days before her period. Both anxiety and guilt feelings can combine to make her incapable of functioning half of each month.

Of course, there are many other reasons for painful periods and the tension that often precedes them. Again, I caution you: first, see your doctor. He will prescribe treatment and determine the seriousness of your ailment.

However, if he finds little or nothing wrong physically, then you have a great deal to gain from UNITROL.

Even if he finds a physical basis for your complaint, UNITROL can help you. If you are suffering, refer to the chapter on pain control. Also, remember the miraculous healing powers

of the subconscious and feed yourself positive, helpful suggestions aimed at helping your doctor to heal you.

But, as I have said, if there is no physical cause for complaint, then you stand to profit enormously from this book. I
suggest you go back, right now, to the beginning and read
it all again. If you have come this far and have not alleviated
psychosomatically-induced ailments, then I am afraid you have
not gone slowly enough through your UNITROL training.

Especially review Your Emotional **Conflict Control Chart.**
Use the pendulum technique to check your responses; perhaps
you have not reached all the truth you seek.

UNITROL Projection Therapy should also help here. But
you must really **want** to know what causes your problem.
Guided association, too, should be employed, and it is often a
painful process—but keep in mind how wonderful it will be
when you are free from crippling illness.

Often, childhood memories of sex play are shrouded in guilt
and recrimination. Such guilt feelings can result in frigidity,
functional sterility, or impotence. But UNITROL can free you
from that guilt, for you are no longer a child, but an adult who
deserves a full, rewarding life.

And you **can** be freed from pain and illness. I urge you to
apply the techniques of UNITROL over and over until you
master control of your mind-body unit. Begin **now** to review
each chapter. Do not give up! I will help you for as long as you
need help. Together, we will make you a new and wonderful
person, free from the chains of psychosomatic ailments.

You Can Control
Stomach and Digestive Tract Problems

Constipation
Diarrhea
General Gastro-intestinal Disturbances
Heartburn

Hiccoughs
Indigestion
Inflammation of the Stomach
Mucous Colitis
Nervous Vomiting
Peptic Ulcer
Spasms
Ulcerative Colitis

It has been said that the way to a man's heart is through his stomach, and it should also be said that the way to heartburn, indigestion, and ulcers is through the stomach of an emotionally upset man or woman. As you can now realize, at this stage of your UNITROL training, an individual can do excessive damage to his or her digestive system by carrying around unresolved emotional problems.

The human mind is such a wondrous thing that it can not only devise computers and poetry and space vehicles, but it also can pervert the normal digestive process so that ulcers are produced, or food is only partially digested, or the intestinal lining becomes inflamed, and sometimes the body is wasted away through excessive elimination or diarrhea. The intestinal tract is truly the sounding board of the emotions.

Not All Psychological

This is not to say, however, that digestive tract problems are **only** emotional. Most of the time, when a patient first visits his doctor, the problem is both emotional and organic, and the organic problem will become more and more severe if not properly treated.

The emotional element is certainly predominant in the early stages, though, and does continue through the duration of the disease. This is the reason that UNITROL therapy can be such a vital adjunct to your physician's treatment. Also, if you care for your mind-body unit properly—on all levels—the chances are slim indeed that you will develop any emotionally-based digestive tract ailment.

This means you can prevent ulcers, mucous colitis, etc., and if you are afflicted with any of these problems now, you can reach a more speedy, more successful recovery by applying UNITROL techniques in addition to any treatment ordered by your physician.

Here, as in all ailments, relaxation is important. The relaxed body is freed from the tension that delays and complicates healing. So, of course, UNITROL relaxation will have a therapeutic effect on you. Also, the importance of involuntary muscle control in relation to intestinal problems should be evident to you now.

It is also important to discover the emotional component of your ailment—and then to find its cause. This can be done through careful application of the UNITROL projection technique. Discover what makes you ''sick to your stomach.'' Ask your subconscious what or who it is that you ''can't stomach.'' Remember the importance of the **literal** effect of words on the subconscious mind.

Remember, also, the case of the man who was sure that he had cancer when he had colitis and diarrhea. Don't make his mistake; **index** your ailment. It is **not** the same as anyone else's, no matter how similar your symptoms are. Just as **you** are an individual, so your illnesses are individual, too.

Of course, UNITROL guided association therapy and the File-and-Forget Technique are important adjuncts to UNITROL projection in treating the psychological components of your particular ailment. Remember, if you have trouble with constipation, that as a child you regarded the bowel movement as an important part of yourself. Thus, in early training, you regarded your stool almost as a ''gift'' for your mother. You pleased her in this way. Now, examine your life. Is there some reason for wanting to deny someone close to you? Are **you** withdrawing from the world, refusing to be part of some emotionally unsatisfactory situation? Perhaps you are reacting physically with the child's behaviour—you are refusing to "give" this part of yourself away. If you find this is true, then the techniques of UNITROL can free you from the chains tying you to the behaviour of the past.

The same general idea may apply to other symptoms. The child often gets his way by developing a stomach ache. This brings him attention and love. Examine your ailments to see if they are tied to such childish behaviour. Remember, you are an adult now, and the things you desire can be gotten in other, more adult, ways.

You have the power to change your life. The mind of man possesses great powers that we are just beginning to tap. With UNITROL, I have shown you how to make these great powers work **for you,** not against you.

Many wise men have believed that the stomach was the seat of the soul, of all emotion. Recognize that there is some truth in this, and feed your stomach the healing, positive emotions that lead to a successful and rewarding life.

chapter 12

How To Overcome Insomnia and Add Life To Your Years

If you have difficulty falling asleep, UNITROL will help solve your problem rapidly. You have probably already noticed that practicing UNITROL brings you to the borderline of sleep almost instantly. Indeed, it may be that you have already conquered your sleep problem, now that you have experienced the technique of UNITROL relaxation.

If you still find it difficult to fall asleep, it is probably because general anxiety or specific problems occupy your thinking mind to such an extent that the subconscious keeps you awake for thinking.

Yes, your subconscious, doing what comes naturally, assumes that you **want** to think under such circumstances. If you keep reviewing problems of the past or present, or projecting yourself into potential problems of the future, your subconscious naturally assumes that this is precisely what you want to do. Therefore, it sends the necessary orders to the body to stay awake. That is why, even though you may be completely relaxed from the skeletal muscle point of view, on the thinking level you are actually wide-awake, seething with emotion and anxiety, reviewing the troubles of the past, pondering the problems of the present, projecting the dangers of the future.

Under these conditions it is obviously difficult to fall asleep. You may not fall asleep until you have exhausted yourself if

165

you persist in occupying your brain with negative thinking. You must substitute soothing, calming, relaxing, sleep-producing thoughts for disturbing, fear- and anxiety-stimulating ideas.

UNITROL will teach you how to do this in several simple ways. First, let me recall to your mind the UNITROL relaxation hibernation technique. By that method you attained the very deepest state of relaxation, and the deepest state of sleep conceivable. Review that chapter. Many of the techniques described in it will be very useful in producing the lesser state of relaxation and sleep required to end your insomnia.

To conquer insomnia you must overcome anxiety. It is time to use the simple, nonspecific formula, "Every day in every way I am getting better and better, happier and happier, healthier and healthier, younger and younger. I know that my subconscious will replace disturbing thoughts by this positive, health-and-happiness-giving affirmation. It becomes a wonderful life when I realize that I am indeed becoming better and better every day in every way, that I am indeed becoming happier and happier, healthier and healthier and, most amazingly, younger and younger."

How to Fall Asleep Without Effort

Remember that **you don't have to try.** You don't have to force your subconscious mind to put you to sleep. Indeed, the worst thing you can do is to **try** hard. Trying is on the conscious level, and has no effect except to keep your subconscious mind more alert as it attempts to remain in step with the incessant activity of the conscious mind. Just **let go**, relax the grip of your conscious mind, let it go blank, and give your subconscious mind the necessary sleep command. You can safely **let go.** The God-power within you, in your subconscious mind, will take over instantly, and you will sleep effortlessly.

Any one of the projection techniques already described will also be helpful in producing sleep. The probability is that you will not need these methods except at times of extreme stress or anxiety. Even then, when you have become skillful in the command phrase technique, projection methods will be unnecessary.

However, you may relax yourself completely and then turn on your subconscious television channel. On that channel you may then project a visual image of yourself asleep. Concentrate on that image, and the image will become a reality. When you see yourself sleeping peacefully, calmly, without motion, with an untroubled serene expression on your face, you will have no difficulty in making this visual image a reality, and you will fall asleep practically instantly.

The Magic Key to Help You Unlock the Door to Sleep

The initial sleep affirmation requires relaxation, and this is attained by the keyword, UNITROL. The next keyword after relaxation is achieved is to produce sleep. Thus, UNITROL—**Sleep.**

The final keyword in this series will be the word **now.** The keyword **now** is derived from the concept of this moment only. If we forget the past, stop disturbing ourselves with anxieties about the future, and concentrate on this moment only, sleep will come. **The important element is to cease thinking.** The keyword, **Now,** is derived from:

No

Old

Worries

Obviously the first letter of each word spells—NOW.

Stop living in the past. Don't look back. Self-torture, by reliving past mistakes, can do you no good. On the contrary, it can prevent sleep, produce illness, and shorten life. The time to make plans for the future is not when you are ready for sleep. Make those plans when you are wide-awake and alert, and not at bedtime. The keyword for sleeping is **Now**.

Or, if you wish the soothing, relaxing sound of the wind in the trees, gently rustling the leaves, or the waves curling upon themselves as they lap against the shore, choose the sound that you find most relaxing and sleep-inducing, and listen to it as you turn up the sound on your subconscious television set. It will lull you to sleep.

And now, forget the fears and failures of the past, the cares of the day, the problems of the morrow—and sleep. Sufficient unto the day are the cares thereof. UNITROL sleep is yours—instantly, from now on.

We all need sleep to rebuild tissue, to rejuvenate our bodies. And we need to be able to go to sleep at will. With UNITROL, you have acquired that ability. But **how much** sleep do we need? An old nursery rhyme tells us:

> Nature needs but five,
> Custom gives the seven,
> Laziness takes nine,
> And Wickedness eleven!

Most of us don't "wickedly" sleep for eleven hours, but it is true that we often feel we require more sleep than we do. Indeed, too often, we "sleep our lives away." If you sleep only eight hours out of twenty-four, you are unconscious one-third of your life!

How to Add Hours to Each Day

How would you like to be able to take a capsule that would produce the same effect as eight hours of sleep? You could then stay up around the clock and enjoy life for an additional eight hours every day, instead of spending one-third of your life unconscious.

UNITROL will make it possible for you to achieve the practical effect of a time capsule, giving you the beneficial results of eight hours of normal sleep in as little as ten or 20 minutes.

This tiny ten-to-twenty-minute time capsule is available to you now—through UNITROL. The latest research on sleep seems to show that out of an eight-hour night of sleep, only about two hours are really deep, rejuvenating sleep. Obviously, if you could take a drug that would instantly plunge you into a deep sleep for two hours, you would have the beneficial effect of the average eight-hour sleep period.

Better still, if you could—at will—instantly place yourself into deep UNITROL sleep, presetting the time mechanism within your brain for two hours, you would attain the same effect.

But UNITROL can do still more than that. There is within the body a time compression mechanism. It is possible to speed physiological processes so rapidly that two hours can easily be compressed into ten or twenty minutes. Accordingly, you may use the UNITROL technique to instruct your body to speed its sleep rejuvenation processes to the point that two hours is compressed into ten or twenty minutes. And so we pass from eight hours to two hours to ten minutes through the magic of UNITROL.

It will help you to understand the UNITROL approach to sleep if you know a little more about present-day sleep research.

Impulses reach the nervous system from all sense organs— the eyes, the ears, the skin, etc.—as electrical currents. These electrical currents flow through many millions of nerve fibers to reach the spinal cord, and then the brain stem and the brain's cortex. The billions of nerve cells in the cortex of the brain then analyze these electrical impulses and send out orders to the body in accordance with this analysis of information received.

Obviously, there is a constant flow of electrical impulses reaching the brain from all parts of the body. And equally obviously, it is essential that we isolate ourselves from such impulses as often as possible, and as completely as possible, to allow an opportunity for rest and rejuvenation within the brain itself, and in every cell, every tissue, every organ of the body directed by the never-sleeping brain. This can be accomplished at frequent intervals by the UNITROL relaxation techniques.

Deep UNITROL sleep—the type that allows for literal rejuvenation of every cell of the body—is our present objective. This is the UNITROL time capsule—the ten- or twenty-minute equivalent of eight hours of normal sleep.

How to Sleep

You cannot go without sleep. On the other hand, you do not really "need" as much sleep as you think. Length of sleep is, for the most part, an acquired habit. You only think that you need to sleep eight hours or ten hours, or whatever number of hours you feel a "need" for. Actually, the real need is for that two hours of deep, rejuvenating sleep. All the rest is spent in tossing and turning and dreaming, at very light levels of sleep.

Many people sleep no more than six hours, and are perfectly healthy. I have not slept more than four hours a night for the past twenty-five years. The UNITROL time capsule of ten or twenty minutes makes even this four hours unnecessary, and I can do without it if required.

You can do the same. But remember that there is great variation in our nervous systems and in the structures of our bodies. Heredity plays an important part in determining the type of structure with which you were born. UNITROL training will ultimately show you the amount of sleep that you actually need. Even after you have learned to take your compressed time capsule, you may find that you will need an additional one or two or four hours' sleep. You will soon learn your individual capacities and needs as you develop in UNITROL training.

If you could learn to maintain vigorous health on a ten- or twenty-minute time capsule, with no additional sleep, you would add many years to your life span. If you were to take a ten- or twenty-minute time capsule at intervals during the course of the day, and sleep an additional profound two hours of UNITROL sleep at night, your life span would become roughly equivalent to ninety-five years.

Just think of it. This single UNITROL sleep technique can bring the equivalent of close to one hundred years of active life.

Your "Quick Sleep" System

Place yourself in a state of deep UNITROL relaxation. You may do this any time of the day when you can spare twenty minutes, or you may utilize it at night during your regular sleep period. Now speak the following command:

"At the command words—UNITROL—Sleep—I will go into a deep state of sleep, with perfect relaxation of all parts of my body. I will sleep for twenty minutes, a profound, dreamless, rejuvenating sleep. This twenty minutes will be the equivalent of two hours of normal deep sleep, and this in turn will be the equivalent of the average eight hours of ordinary sleep. In other words, from now on the command, UNITROL—Sleep, will produce twenty minutes of profound, deep sleep, the equivalent of eight hours of ordinary sleep. I will waken relaxed, alert, feeling wonderful, rejuvenated."

You can adapt these words for your individual needs. The thought is the important feature. Practice this technique until you drop off to sleep instantly on the command, UNITROL—Sleep. The time mechanism within your own brain will waken you within the prescribed twenty minutes. The effect on every cell, every tissue, every organ of your body will be that of eight hours of ordinary sleep. You will be relaxed, alert, full of new-found pep and energy—literally rejuvenated. Prepare

to live one hundred years of active, healthy, normal life—
thanks to UNITROL sleep.

To Sum It Up . . .

Sleep is important to health and vitality. It can be yours
through learning and acting on the UNITROL sleep **Now**
formula:

NO
OLD
WORRIES

Leave your past behind; your subconscious will respond to
positive, soothing suggestions.

But remember, too much sleep can rob you of much of your
life. With UNITROL, you have learned how to sleep the rejuvenating hours of sleep—sleep that covers a small period of
time but rests you completely.

It was said that Thomas Alva Edison slept only four or five
hours a night, and look what he accomplished!

So sleep—sleep well with UNITROL, and free yourself by
giving yourself both **rest** and **more waking hours.**

chapter 13

This may be the end
of the book, but it's just
the beginning for you—
a new beginning. By now,

UNITROL: Your Drink
From the Fountain of Youth

you should have mastered the concepts of UNITROL and you
should be able to apply them to fight illness and grow in health
and strength. However, the true beginning is now. In this
chapter the theme is rejuvenation—how to keep yourself
young or make yourself younger.

Man has several ages. He has a physiological age, which may
be either less or more than his chronological age. This means
that his body tissues may function at a youthful thirty year
level, when he is actually forty or forty-five years of age. Or,
on the other hand, his body tissues may work at a fifty year
level when he is actually only thirty-five years old.

You have seen many people who are older than their years,
or younger than their years. This represents the contrast between physiological age and chronological age. Then, of course,
there is mental age. A person may be fifty years old, and yet
mentally only twelve years of age, or the reverse may be true.
I can tell you this—if you wish literally to rejuvenate yourself you must begin to **think young**. When you think young
you will be young.

You have been learning throughout this book of the power
of words and the power of your subconscious mind. Now you
can recognize fully how important it is to **think young**. With

UNITROL, you have the power to achieve more than you imagine. We know that man grows old, but no one knows **why** this is so. We know that the mind **directly** affects the body, but no one knows the FULL POWERS of the mind. We are just beginning to realize a small part of the miraculous power that dwells within man.

We have all read of men who, in biblical times, lived to be hundreds of years old—yet **they did not have** the knowledge that we have today! If a man caught pneumonia before the discovery of penicillin, he had little chance of surviving. Yet men survived! They survived pneumonia and many other ailments, and they lived to ripe old age. Where is the secret of long life hidden?

I believe it resides within man, within the God-power that he possesses, within his faith and belief in **himself**.

The Man Who Decided to Die

Let me give you an example of what I mean. In this case, the faith was all negatively directed, but **very** strong.

I was treating a woman I'll call Mrs. Brenner. She came to me complaining of several difficulties relating to the lower intestine. During surgery, I discovered that she had malignant cancer of the bowel. It was only a matter of time until she would die. But Mrs. Brenner was a strong willed woman with an iron constitution otherwise, even though she was sixty-five years old. I discussed her case with her husband, and we decided that it was best to tell her of the seriousness of her condition.

During the months that followed, I treated Mrs. Brenner often, trying to help her to adjust to her pain. She was a wonderful, brave woman. However, at this time her husband began saying, "I'll die before she does."

Since Mr. Brenner was two years younger than his wife, and

in excellent health, no one paid attention to what seemed like morbid statements. I asked him to come in for a check-up, which he did, and **there was nothing wrong with him**! Still he kept saying, "I'll die before she does."

His children reassured him, as I did, but he had decided this was so. Two months before Mrs. Brenner passed away, Mr. Brenner died in his sleep.

The postmortem examination failed to reveal anything wrong. Cause of death: old age. Not that Mr. Brenner was that old, physically. His body was much younger than his chronological age. But he **had decided** that **he was old** and that **it was time to die!**

Man is a marvellous mechanism that we little understand, but I am convinced that if one has control over the mind-body unit—UNITROL—then even those things we call miracles are possible, for us. And the miracle of youth is possible, the miracles of vitality and rejuvenation are yours IF YOU BELIEVE. BELIEVE, but not negatively as Mr. Brenner did, but **positively**, and a new life can be yours.

How to Find Youth
Through the UNITROL T.D.

And now let me tell you some of the specific elements of UNITROL Rejuvenation Therapy. First, I should like to tell you about the magic of Time Distortion. How would you like to take ten, fifteen, or twenty years off your age, almost instantly? The fountain of youth is literally yours, in a subjective sense, and even to a large extent in an objective sense. This means that you can literally become as young as you wish in your mind, and even to a large extent in your body. It is all done through the magic of the subconscious mind, with the UNITROL Projection Method.

If you are over forty, I would suggest that you become

twenty-nine! You can succeed in doing this, and yet maintain the maturity and wisdom that you have gained from the experience of your chronologically longer life span.

You must associate with young people, so that you can see the way they think and behave. You must behave and think as they do, if you are to rejuvenate mentally and emotionally to their level. Of course, there are limitations to this, and you must use good judgment so that you do not exceed your physical limitations too early in the Rejuvenation Process.

If you are over forty-five, then I would suggest that each birthday should be celebrated as your twenty-ninth from this point on. Do not use a single candle on your cake; use twenty-nine. It is most important that you use your imagination to implant ideas of youth in your subconscious, and the best possible time to do it—in addition to the times during which you practice UNITROL—will be during your birthday parties.

Launch an Enthusiasm Effort

Enthusiasm is one of the major attributes of youth. You must become enthusiastic in everything you do. Think enthusiasm and you will be enthusiastic. Give yourself positive suggestions. Be enthusiastic at all times. Give yourself these suggestions not only during state of UNITROL relaxation, but at every possible opportunity. Say to yourself, "Every day in every way I am getting younger and younger." You will soon notice that you will act younger and be younger.

Say to yourself, "Every day in every way I am enjoying life more and more." Soon you will have an enthusiasm and capacity for the enjoyment of life that will astonish your former and present friends and associates.

Learn to enjoy this moment as if it were going to be the last. After all, the past is gone, and the future may never come. You have this moment only in which to enjoy life. Live it to the fullest, one moment, one heartbeat at a time.

See Yourself Young

A major part of the UNITROL Rejuvenation Method is to visualize yourself younger than you are at this moment. You will do this by lying down or sitting down and going into UNITROL relaxation. When you are fully relaxed with your eyes closed, see yourself as you want to be—years younger. If you have photographs of yourself at an earlier age, this will help. However, do not be unreasonable in your demands. Proceed gradually and you will have a better chance for long-lasting success. Do not ask to become twenty or thirty years younger all at once. Be content with a few years of rejuvenation at a time. You will be amazed at the ultimate effect, if you do not demand too much from your subconscious. Be reasonable with your subconscious and your subconscious will be your obedient creator of a miraculous new and youthful mind, body and spirit.

Now, while you are fully relaxed, visualize the new you. See yourself as young as your want to be. Notice that your skin is now much more flexible and youthful in appearance.

Notice that your eyes are brighter. Watch yourself walk while you visualize the new you. Notice the new bounce, the spring in your step, the youthful motion of your legs and arms and body. See the way you now hold your head higher, and the enthusiasm and sparkle in your eyes.

Listen to your rejuvenated voice, the voice of youth. It sings with excitement and enthusiasm. Hear that! Hear it well! It is a new voice that you will be hearing in the future whenever you speak—the rejuvenated **you** speaking.

Now give yourself the following suggestion, speaking aloud, "Every day in every way I am getting younger and younger, happier and happier, healthier and healthier. The image I see of the new me, younger and younger, is sinking deep into my subconscious, and my subconscious will gradually make this a reality. Every day in every way I am becoming younger and younger.''

When you practice this regularly, you will become expert in the technique of Time Distortion, and you will literally shed years in your attitude, your behavior, the functions of your body, and the tissues of your body. You will actually be drinking the waters of the fountain of youth.

Take a Drink of Youth

Indeed, to visualize yourself drinking from the fountain of youth, just place yourself in UNITROL relaxation, and imagine how the fountain of youth should look. See aged people walking up to this miraculous fountain and drinking the waters. See them restored to youth. See the amazing change in their appearance. Watch the change in the color of their hair, the new color and texture of their skin, the renewed brightness of their eyes, the slimness of their new figures, the vitality and spring in their walk, the enthusiasm in their voices.

Now see yourself walking up to the fountain and drinking the same waters. Observe the same changes in yourself. Again, I must caution you not to demand too much from your sub-conscious all at one time. Be content with gradual changes, and every day in every way you will literally become younger and younger, as if you were drinking from the fountain of youth in actuality.

Remember that we each function in our own unique and personal time zone. Some of us live fast and furiously. Some of us live at a slower pace. Some of us, in consequence, age rapidly, while others retain their youth and vigor far beyond the average. When you practice the UNITROL Rejuvenation Therapy, you create a favorable time zone for yourself. Let it be a time zone in which you enjoy a new-found youth and health and happiness, enthusiasm and vigor, new capacity for the enjoyment of life every day in every way.

How UNITROL Hibernation
Rejuvenates You

Now, I want you to play a very special role in a special drama. You have lost your way in the Arctic. You are on a vast reach of ice, as far as the eye can see in all directions. It is bare, quiet, very cold. Although you are dressed in warm furs, you have gone as far as you can. You are tired and you want to lie down and rest.

You know that if you are to survive you must stay exactly where you are until a search party finds you. But to survive and be at rest in this intense cold, even though you are dressed in warm furs, requires that you lower the level of all body functions. You must lower this level to such an extent that your heart beat becomes very slow, your respiration barely perceptible. All body functions must be brought to a low level, exactly as if you were a bear going into hibernation. This is the ultimate state of deep, deep, deep relaxation. This is the ultimate state of skeletal and involuntary smooth muscle control. This is the ultimate state of lowered body metabolism.

You can achieve this state with practice. You can achieve it right now by playing your role to your best capacity. See yourself as a great actor or actress. You can play this part perfectly.

Remember, also, that your subconscious mind controls every cell, every tissue, every organ, every function of your body. It controls the rate of blood flow, the beating of your heart, the size of the coronary arteries that feed blood to your heart muscle, the level of your blood pressure, the rate of your respiration, the flow of secretions from your vital ductless glands—every cell, every tissue, every organ, every function of your body.

Remember that your subconscious is your servant. It will do your bidding without question. You need merely tell it what to do, and then leave the rest to your all-powerful, obedient servant. Your subconscious mind has full powers, and always **can** do your bidding. It will do it now. It will produce this deep, deep, deep state of hibernation-relaxation.

This depth of body-mind-spirit control is an ultimate goal. If you can achieve it right now, you can stop aging. When you learn to maintain this state of hibernation-relaxation for a sufficiently long period of time (days or even weeks), you will literally rejuvenate every cell, every tissue, every organ of your body. They will become younger, healthier, more vital and stronger.

When you achieve this state of hibernation-relaxation, you will have full control of the involuntary muscles of the body, including the smooth muscles lining your arteries. Since you are as old as your arteries, you can readily see the importance of this control over their flexibility.

This is a wonderful state of relaxation. It is a state that you can achieve by playing this role to the full. Visualize yourself exactly as I have above described. Let this image rest in your subconscious together with the command, UNITROL—**Hibernation-Relaxation!**

Such complete relaxation obviously has a rejuvenating effect. But UNITROL Rejuvenation includes more than just making the body younger. It also includes reshaping of the mind and spirit.

You have the power to make yourself vital and alive **every waking moment!** I have shown you the way to employ the various techniques of UNITROL to free yourself from both physical and mental pain, to rid yourself of the negative influences that have kept your life from being what you desired. Now it is up to **you. Your** strength, **your** determination, **your** belief in the God-power within you will reshape your life.

Breathe Yourself Young

I have one last word for you, but a most important word. Beginning each new day is like beginning a new life. When you wake in the morning, the world is full of possibility. Happiness is yours for the taking. Begin this new day—this new life—by taking a few moments to **breathe.**

Not just any kind of breathing will do; this must be a special moment of inhaling and exhaling.

When you first wake up each day, you should begin the day with a few moments breathing in this special way: Breathe in slowly, repeating to yourself, "YOUNGER and YOUNGER, HAPPIER and HAPPIER, HEALTHIER and HEALTHIER." Now exhale, very slowly, saying to yourself, "UNITROL makes it so!" You should repeat this exercise at least five times, more if you have the time.

You will find that your day will begin **peacefully** and **positively.** You need not **try** to make this so. Remember the power of your subconscious mind—YOUR POWER, for it is **your** mind. It will go to work for you, making life easier, better— making life LIVE!

In the beginning of this book I offered you my hand, a human helping hand, to guide you through this self-improvement program. My hand is still extended to you, in friendship, offering assistance whenever and wherever you need it. The rest is up to you. You have it within you to move forward, toward a new and brighter life!

A Final Word . . .

Heaven and Hell are to be found in each man's mind. God and his Angels, as well as the creatures of Hell, are therefore the natural inhabitants of the mind of man. The Freudian psychoanalyst will label these areas and creatures as the **super-ego**, the **ego** and the **id**—still more semantic confusion.

Man has it within himself to be God-like. He also has it within himself to be a creature of the Devil. Do not look upon these names and labels as actual inhabitants of the human mind. They are merely generally accepted descriptive words and phrases for potential forms of behavior.

It is my belief that immortality, like charity, begins at home. By this I mean that it is of fundamental importance to keep the mind-body-spirit unit functioning at its best physiological and psychological levels. This can only be done by following the proper rules of hygiene and diet, and by the recognition that there is within each human mind an untapped potential for self-healing. There is, also, a generally untapped potential for the healing of others. Physicians demonstrate this to a small degree in terms of their scientific training. **Healers** demonstrate this in another direction, usually without scentific training. And then, of course, there is the great Healer, Jesus Christ.

The concept of a Universal Brotherhood of Man is not a question of integrating peoples of all colors and beliefs. It is the simple recognition of the fact that the God qualities of healing, love, compassion, understanding, charity, are human characteristics, the potential of **every** man's mind, regardless of his skin color or his religious beliefs.

In my humble opinion it is essential that man leave behind him in historical perspective the God of vengeance. If man is to survive as a God-man, it will only be in terms of understanding, love and compassion for his fellow man.

The spirit of man is immortal. It moves on and on through countless centuries, fired and strengthened by each passage through its crucible of flesh. The teachings of UNITROL offer the body-mind-spirit unit the opportunity for a giant leap forward in spiritual evolution. The practical applications of UNITROL in self-healing are evident. The larger applications of UNITROL in the healing of the self-inflicted wound that separates each man from his brother are made more evident by the teachings of the UNITROL Teaching Foundation * and the Universal Brotherhood of Man.

You have embarked upon this study with the reading of this basic text. It is the hope of the author, and the promise of the Spirit of God within you, that you will continue on the Path. Once again, I reach out my hand to you and ask that you join me in our mutual quest through infinity for better health and longer life, for peace and happiness, for better understanding of our fellow man, and for immortality.

---

* UNITROL Teaching Institute. Alfred J. Cantor, M D., Director, 147–41 Sanford Ave., Flushing, N. Y.

Index

A

Acceptance therapy, 135
Actions, delayed reactions, 44
Adaptation therapy, 89
Adolescence, conflict check chart, 65–66
Adrenalin, 23
Adult life, conflict check chart, 66–68
Affirmation therapy, 59
  to conquer anxieties, 127, 130, 135
  easing domestic tensions, 135–136
  financial worries, 133
  health worries, 134–135
  for overcoming worries, 129–130
  for relieving pain, 139–140, 142
  for sleep, 166
Aging processes, 26–27
  arresting, 46
  chronological *vs.* physiological, 173
  effect of tension, 85
  rejuvenation technique, 173–183
  relaxing muscles, 26
  reversing or halting, 26–27
Alcoholism:
  aid for, 64
  expectation therapy, 79
  use of projection technique, 72
Allergies, 27–28, 152–154
  cause and cure, 152–154
  effect of subconscious mind, 61
  use of guided association therapy, 153–154
  use of projection techniques, 72
Ambition, frustrated, 101
Amnesia, selective, 111–122
  causes, 111

Amnesia, selective (*Cont.*):
  definition, 111
  living in the past, 120–122
  techniques, 111–118
Anesthesia, 144–149
  case history, 146–147
  producing, 144–146
  technique, 147–149
  use of UNITROL in place of, 144–149
Anesthetics, technique to use instead of, 144–146
Anger, reacting to, 34
Angina pectoris, 25, 140
Animals, reactions, 34–35
Anxiety, 125–136
  affirmation therapy, 127, 130
  causes, 23
  easing domestic tensions, 135–136
  effect of muscle control, 26–27
  effect on sleep, 166
  health worries, 133–135
  indexing technique, 41–42
  methods of conquering, 125–136
  money worries, 131–133
  reactions, 35
  relaxation technique, 50
Arteries:
  flexibility of, 180
  spasms, 24–25
Arthritis, 26, 157–158
Asthma, 152–154
  effect of subconscious on, 60
  expectation therapy, 79
Attitudes:
  changing, 113, 125
  control of, 29
  negative, 31
Attracting others, 81

Autobiographical studies, 102, 105,
      108

                      B

Behavior, emotional, 35
Belief:
   control of, 29
   power of, 174–175
Blessings, counting, 114–116
Blood pressure, 28, 154–156
   ability to lower, 26
   controlled by subconscious, 85
   effect of subconscious mind, 57
   effect of tensions on, 23–24
Body:
   controlling functions, 22
   developing numbness, 144–146
   lowering metabolism of, 89, 179
   reactions to words and symbols,
      35–37
   secret language of, 74–75
   strength of, 28
Brain:
   arteries, 24–25
   effect of emotional tensions, 24
   "feeling and thinking" regions,
      34–35
   nervous system, 33–34
   spasm of arteries, 24–25
   strokes, 24
   subconscious level, 34
   thalamus and cortex, 34
   thinking regions, 34–35, 44
Breathing, relaxation technique,
      49–50, 52, 181
Brotherhood of man, 182–183

                      C

Cancer, 27–28, 41, 115
   effect of subconscious, 76–77
   pain control technique, 142
Cantor, Alfred J., 126, 183n
Carnegie, Dale, 130
Changes, 127
   adjusting to, 116–117, 120
   state of continual, 42–44
Character traits, changing, 85, 125,
      135
Childhood experiences:
   conflict check chart, 64–65
   repressed emotional disturbances,
      100, 107

Childhood experiences (*Cont.*):
   revealed by projection method,
      73, 77
Colitis, 162–163
   causes, 25
   effect of word on emotions, 40–41
   use of projection techniques, 77
Commands given to subconscious,
      45–56, 58–59, 84, 151
   repeating aloud, 87–88
Confidence, lack of, 31
Conflict check charts, 64–68, 161
   checking, 108
   guided association therapy, 101–
      102
   to spot problem areas, 69
   used with projection method, 72–
      73, 76
Constipation, 161–162
   causes, 25
   effect of subconscious, 74
Coronary occlusion, 25
   pain control technique, 140
Counting your blessings, 114–116

                      D

Dating techniques, 42–44, 95, 105
   beneficial effect, 43
   guided association therapy and,
      105, 107
   listing upsetting things, 43–44
Death of a loved one:
   reliving, 92–93, 97, 102–103
   source of disturbing symptoms,
      102, 109
Decision-making, 127
Diarrhea, 161–162
   effect of subconscious, 76–78
Digestive tract, 161–164
Disassociation technique, for con-
      trolling pain, 145
Diseases, organic, 27–28
Domestic tensions, how to ease,
      135–136
Dreams, interpreting, 73
Drugs, use of, 28

                      E

Eczema, 152–154
Edison, Thomas Alva, 172
Emotional disturbances:
   associated symptoms, 99–108

Emotional disturbances (*Cont.*):
  dating technique, 43
  delayed reactions, 33–34, 44
  due to muscle tension, 48
  guided association therapy, 92–95
  pendulum method for solving, 64–68
  reliving, 92–95
  uncovering repressed, 100
  voluntary muscle control, 45
Emotional release, reliving experiences and, 103–106
Emotional tensions (*see* Tensions)
Emotions:
  affected by muscle tension, 47–48
  conflict between will and, 30
  development and control, 35
  effect of voluntary muscle tension, 47–48
  influence of words on, 38–40
  reactions, 34–35
  silent level, 92, 95–96
Endocrine glands, affected by subconscious mind, 57
Enthusiasm therapy, 127, 156
Esophagus, ulcer of, 25
Executives, decision-making, 127
Expectation therapy, 78–79, 151
Experience:
  chains of, 97–99
  reliving, 103–106
Eyes, muscle control, 45–48

F

Face:
  emotions reflected in, 48
  muscle control, 46–48
  worry lines, 46
Failure, 107
  attitude toward, 116
  dating technique, 43
  file-and-forget method, 120
Faith, 142, 174
  importance of, 29–30
Fatigue, 158–160
Fear, reactions to, 35, 101, 155, 160
File-and-forget technique, 104–106, 119–120, 154
  principles of, 112–113
Fire, reactions to word, 35–37
Food, digestion of, 26
Forgetting, 119–120, 154
  filing and, 104–106

Forgetting (*Cont.*):
  principle of, 112
  selective, 113
  unpleasant experiences, 112–113
  value of, 91, 112
Frigidity, 160–161
Frustrations:
  dating technique, 43
  file-and-forget method, 120
Future:
  creating and controlling, 73–74
  projections, 73–74, 108–109

G

Gallstones, reducing pain, 137, 142
Generalizations, danger of, 41–43
Genito-urinary tract ailments, 160–161
Glands:
  controlled by subconscious, 57, 83
  effect of tensions, 23
God:
  healing force, 31, 182
  power of God within you, 29–31, 134
Grief, 35
Guided association therapy, 91–109, 163
  being hypnotized by past, 108–109
  contacting silent level, 91–95
  dating technique, 107
  determining cause of allergies, 153–154
  examination of life situations, 101
  list of key words, 105–106
  listing disturbing situations, 102
  nature of, 93–94
  reliving emotional conflict, 93–95
  reliving experiences, 103–104
  repressed memories, 100, 103
  safety devices, 105
  steps in, 103–104
  to uncover causes of illness, 106–108
Guilt feelings, 160–161

H

Happiness, expecting, 79
Hate:
  listing people hated, 102

Hate (*Cont.*):
  use of dating technique, 43
Hay fever, 121, 152–154
Headaches, 158–160
  expectation therapy, 79
  migraine, 140, 158–160
  reducing pain, 137, 140
  relaxing muscles, 47
  use of projection techniques, 72
Healing, 31, 182
  effect of subconscious on, 60
  relaxation aids in, 141
  use of words, 33–34
Health:
  blessing of good, 114–116
  controlled by projection method,
    71–82
  effect of words on, 37–38
  expectation therapy, 78–79
  overcoming worries about, 133–
    135
  relaxing for, 49–50
Heart attacks, 28, 151
  angina pectoris, 25, 140
  controlled by projection method,
    74–75
  controlled by subconscious, 83,
    85–86
  coronary occlusion, 25, 140
  fear of, 155
  flexibility of arteries, 180
  prevention and control, 74–75, 83,
    85–87, 154–156
  reducing pain, 137, 140–141
  relaxing arteries, 26
  spasms of arteries, 24–25
  UNITROL relaxation, 155–156
Heartbeats:
  ability to slow, 25–26
  effect of subconscious mind, 57
  increases in rate, 23, 25
Heartburn, 161–162
Hemorrhoids, causes, 25
Hibernation technique, 166, 179–180
Hives, 152–154
Hobbies, value of, 118
Hypertension, prevention and control, 154–156
Hypnosis, 108–109

I

Ideas, relationship between muscles
  and, 61–62

Illnesses:
  effect of emotion on, 38–40
  finding secret behind, 106–108
  overcoming worries about, 133–
    135
  UNITROL for relieving, 151–164
Immortality, 182
*Immortality—Pathways to Peace of
  Mind* (Cantor), 126
Impotence, 160–161
Indexing technique, 41–42, 95, 163
Individual differences, 41
Inferiority, feelings of, 31
Insomnia, 158–160
  overcoming, 165–172
Intestinal tract, 161–163
  controlled by subconscious, 84–85
  involuntary muscle control, 25–
    26, 163
  reducing pain, 137
  relaxation of muscles, 26

J

Jesus Christ, 126, 182
Jobs, unsatisfactory, 101
Joint and muscle pains, 157–158
Joy of living, 80–81

K

Keller, Helen, 117
Key word commands, 45–56, 151
  guided association therapy, 105–
    106
  muscle control, 52–53
  for relaxing, 52–55
  for sleep, 167–168

L

Laughter, value of, 80–81
Le Cron, Leslie, 61
Lewis, Joe E., 132
Life:
  living one day at a time, 126–127
  living to the fullest, 114
Lincoln, Abraham, 30
Lourdes, miracles at, 29
Love:
  listing people loved, 102
  reactions to word, 38–39, 42–43
Lungs, controlled by subconscious,
  83, 89

M

Marital problems, 135
  listing, 135
  use of pendulum and projection
    techniques, 135
Marriage relationships, 101
Memories:
  discarding painful, 119-120
  guided association technique, 91,
    93-94
  file-and-forget method, 119-120
  rendering harmless, 91
  repressed, 76
  selective amnesia, 111-122
Memory training, 112-113
Menopausal problems, 160-161
Menstrual problems, 160-161
Mental depression, 158-160
Mental diseases, 22
Metabolism, reducing, 89, 179
Migraine, 140, 158-160
Mind, powers of, 174
Mind-body unit, 21-22
  controlling, 22
  psychosomatic illness affect, 27-
    28
  treated as single unit, 22
  verbal distinctions, 21
Mistakes:
  attitude toward, 116
  file-and-forget method, 119-122
Money worries, use of UNITROL
    therapy, 131-133
Muscle control:
  command technique, 51-53
  difference between tension and
    relaxation, 45-47
  effect on emotions, 47-48
  emotions affected by tension, 47-
    48
  eyes, 45-48
  feeling tension in, 45-47
  forehead and cheek muscles, 46-
    48
  involuntary, 24-25, 83-90
    by subconscious, 83-85
  muscle tension, 45-46
  recognizing relaxed muscles, 46
  relaxation technique, 49-55
  voluntary, 22-24, 45
Muscles:
  arteries, 24-25
  internal, 83

Muscles (*Cont.*):
  intestinal tract, 25
  involuntary, 24-25
  relationship between ideas and,
    61-62
  relaxation of, 26
  relieving pain, 137, 140-141, 157-
    158
  skeletal, 23
  spasms, 24-26
  voluntary, 22-23

N

Negative attitudes, 31
Negative thinking, 84
  illnesses due to, 112-114, 118
Nerves, UNITROL therapy, 158-
    160
Nervous system, 21
  reactions of, 33-34, 44
  structure and function, 33-34
  words and sensations recorded,
    33
Nervous tension, 158-160
Neurodermatitis, 152-154
Neuroses, 158-160
Niebuhr, Dr. Reinhold, 117
Numbness, developing, 144-146

O

Optimism, 118-119
  counting your blessings, 114-116
Osler, Sir William, 126
Overweight, 28, 121, 158-160
  due to emotional strain, 27
  effect of subconscious mind, 60
  use of projection technique, 72

P

Pain control, 28, 31, 138-149
  disassociation technique, 145
  nature's warning signal, 137
  power of positive affirmation,
    139-140
  practicing technique, 140
  projection technique, 141-143,
    158
  reducing pain, 137-149
  role of pain, 143
  secret of diverting pain, 138
  silent level therapy, 96

Pain control (*Cont.*)
  stroking painful area, 139–141
  switch technique, 144
  technique for producing numbness, 144–146
  UNITROL therapy, 157–158
  used in place of anesthesia, 144–149
Past, living in, 120–122
Peace of mind, 26, 28
  achieving, 127, 132
Pendulum method, 61–64, 161
  conflict check chart, 64–68
  effect on subconscious mind, 61–64
  principle of, 61–62
  relaxing muscles, 63
  for self-knowledge, 61–64
Personality, 22
Physicians:
  consultation with, 28, 74
  UNITROL used under supervision of, 28
Positive replacement theory, 31
Positive suggestions, 30
Powers:
  belief, 174–175
  of God within, 29–31, 134
  of mind, 174
  of present, 113–114
Pregnancies, fear of, 101, 160
Premenstrual tension, 160
Present:
  appreciating, 113–114
  keeping busy, 117–118
  living one day at a time, 126–127
  power of, 113–114
Problem solving:
  analysis of problem, 128
  examination of life situation, 101
  key words for restimulating problems, 105–106
  listing disturbing situations, 102
  use of conflict check charts, 68, 105
Projection method, 63, 71–82, 163
  asking questions, 75–76
  to discover source of ailment, 156
  enthusiasm therapy, 78, 80–81
  expectation therapy, 78–79
  for future events, 73–74
  for producing anesthesia, 148
  for relieving pain, 141–143

Projection method (*Cont.*):
  use of conflict check chart, 72–73, 76
  visualizing TV screen, 71–73, 177–178
Psoriasis, 152
Psychiatry, 94
Psychoanalysis, 91–92, 94–95, 182
  insight, 94–97
Psychological ailments, 158–160
Psychosomatic illnesses:
  causes, 91
  effect on mind-body unit, 27–28
  emotional reactions, 35, 37–38
  listing earliest illnesses and accidents, 107
  relaxation technique for, 88
  triggered by emotional conflicts, 105–108
  use of projection techniques, 72
Psychosomatic medicines, 21
Psychotherapy, 91–92

R

Rage, effect of, 35
Reactions:
  delayed, 34–35, 37
  to words and symbols, 33
Reality, escaping from, 79
Reasoning, applying, 42
Reflex action, 34–35
Rejuvenation therapy, 26, 28, 94, 173–183
  association with younger people, 176
  being enthusiastic, 176
  due to muscle relaxation, 26–27
  hibernation-relaxation, 166, 179–180
  time distortion technique, 175–176, 178
  visualizing self as young, 177–178
Relaxation technique, 49–52, 73–75, 118–119
  adaptation therapy, 89
Relaxation technique, 49–52
  basic commands, 51–52
  deep breathing, 49–50, 52
  deep state of relaxation, 53–54, 87–88, 180
  hibernation technique, 166, 179–180

Relaxation technique (*Cont.*):
  key word control, 52–55, 71
  from neck down, 54–55
  practicing, 55–56, 87–89
  voluntary muscles, 45–47
Reliving experiences, 105–106
  key words, 105–106
  with full feeling, 104–106
Repetition, 87–88
  effect on subconscious mind, 58–59
Resignation, value of, 116–117
Rheumatism, 157–158
Rose fever, 152

S

Safety devices:
  dating techniques, 41–42
  indexing techniques, 41–42
Self-denial, 31
Self-understanding, three steps of, 98–100
Sensations:
  recorded in nervous system, 33
  recorded on body tissues, 96–97
  on silent level, 96
Sexual adjustment, 101
Shock state, 89
Sickness (*see* Illnesses)
Silent level therapy, 91–96
  contacting, 91–95
  emotions and sensations, 92–93, 98
  experiences, 95–96, 99
  letting it work, 98
  principles of, 95–100
Sleep, 165–172
  affirmation for, 166
  amount needed, 168–171
  effect of anxiety on, 166
  effect of subconscious on, 60
  expectation therapy, 79
  gaining more waking hours, 168–171
  hibernation technique, 88, 166
  key word for, 167–168
  limited to short periods, 168–171
  overcoming insomnia, 165–172
  "quick sleep" system, 171
  relaxation technique, 50, 55, 166–167
  research on, 169–170
  time mechanism, 171

Smiling:
  importance of, 48, 80–81
  use of *smile* words, 118–119
Smoking, 72, 155
Somatic diseases, 21
Spirit of man, 22
  immortality, 182–183
  mind, body and, 29–30
Sterility, functional, 160–161
Stomach, 161–164
Stress:
  adaptation therapy, 89
  effect of muscle control, 26–27
Strokes, causes, 24
Stuttering, 158–160
Subconscious mind, 34, 37, 57–69
  characteristics, 57–59
  commands given to, 52–55, 58–59, 84, 151
  repeating aloud, 87–88
  communicating with, 59–60, 71
    pendulum method, 61–64, 71–82
    projection technique, 63, 75–76
  conflict check chart, 64–68
  effect of repetition, 58–59
  enthusiasm therapy, 80–81
  expectation therapy, 78–79
  involuntary muscle control, 83–90
  key word control, 52–55
  literal effect of words on, 163
  pendulum method for conversing with, 61–64
  powers of God, 87
  relationship between problems and past events, 75
  repressed memories, 76
  retraining, 85–86
  silent level, 91–92, 95–96
  special language, 58
  teaching, 58–59
  use of positive statements, 59
  using power of, 59–60
Success:
  achieving, 133
  expecting, 79, 133
Switch technique, for controlling pain, 144
Symbols:
  as posthypnotic commands, 108–109
  reactions to, 33–34
  response of body to, 35–37
Symptoms, 33
  direct removal therapy, 31

Symptoms *(Cont.)*:
  effect of reliving emotional sore
    spots, 94
  effect of subconscious, 76–78
  emotional disturbances and, 33,
    99–108
  examination of life situation, 101
  guided association therapy, 94

T

Tachycardia, prevention and control, 154–156
Tears, release of, 104, 154
Tennyson, Alfred Lord, 118
Tensions:
  causes, 23
  effect on aging processes, 85
  effect on overeating, 27
  effect on skeletal muscles, 23
  emotional, 23
  muscle, 45–46
  relaxation technique, 50
  release from, 26
  ways to decrease, 24
Thinking:
  constructive, 117
  control of, 29
  feelings and, 30
Tics, 23, 159
Time distortion technique, 175–176,
  178
Tissue changes, 33
  effect of emotions, 35
  pain and, 137
  reversing, 106
Tranquility, achieving, 45
Tranquilizers, not necessary with
  UNITROL, 28, 125

U

Ulcers, 115
  peptic, 25, 162–163
UNITROL:
  accomplishments, 28
  basic command technique, 51–52
  control of muscles, 24–27
  control of thinking, 29

UNITROL *(Cont.)*:
  definition, 22, 31
  direct symptom removal therapy,
    31
  importance of, 28
  involuntary muscle control, 83–90
  nature of, 21–31
  positive replacement theory, 31
  projection technique, 71–82
  to relieve sickness, 151–164
  used under physician's supervi-
    sion, 28
UNITROL Teaching Foundation,
  183
Universal Brotherhood of Man,
  182–183

W

Words, 33–44
  effect on health, 33, 37
  effect on nervous system, 33, 37
  emotional content, 38, 103
  generalizations, 41–43
  healing properties, 33–34
  influence on emotions, 38–40
  as posthypnotic commands, 108–
    109
  power of, 31
  reactions to, 33–34, 44
  recorded in nervous system, 33
  response of body to, 35–37
  use of *smile* words, 118–119
Work, value of keeping busy, 117–
  118
Worries:
  affirmation therapy, 129–130
  chart of, 128–129
  destructive nature of, 129
  health, 133–135
  money, 131–133
  relaxation technique, 50
  technique to overcome, 125–136

Y

Youth, 173–183
  rejuvenation technique, 173–183
  renewal of, 26, 28